Sing the Story

HYMNAL: A WORSHIP BOOK
SUPPLEMENT II

Sing the Story
Hymnal: A Worship Book—Supplement 2

Unless otherwise noted, Scripture text is quoted, with permission, from the New Revised Standard Version, ©1989, Division of Christian Education of the National Council of Churches of Christ in the United States of America.

The publisher gratefully acknowledges permission to reproduce texts, tunes, and arrangements granted by publishers, organizations, and individuals listed as copyright holders below each hymn. Addresses for these copyright holders can be found in the Acknowledgment pages of this volume. Where material does not list another copyright holder, permission must be obtained from Faith & Life Resources. Every effort has been made to trace the owner or holder of each copyright. If any rights have been inadvertently infringed upon, the publisher asks that the omission be excused and agree to make the necessary corrections in subsequent printings.

International Standard Book Number: 978-0-8361-9369-5

Music engraving by James E. Clemens
Cover design by Gwen Stamm

Printed in Canada by Friesens, Altona, Manitoba

Cover symbol – The lamb in the midst of briars is a traditional Anabaptist symbol. It illustrates the suffering Lamb of God, who calls the faithful to obedient service.

13 12 11 10 09 08   10 9 8 7 6 5 4 3 2

To order or request information, please call
1 800 245-7894 (U.S.) and 1 800 631-6535 (Canada).
www.mph.org

Faith & Life Resources
A division of Mennonite Publishing Network
Mennonite Church USA and
Mennonite Church Canada

INTRODUCTION

*For no one can lay any foundation other than the one that has been laid;
that foundation is Jesus Christ.* —1 Corinthians 3:11

This worship book is the second supplement to *Hymnal: A Worship Book*. The first, *Sing the Journey*, was published in 2005, and focuses on the life and mission of the Church in the world. *Sing the Story* embraces the heart of our worship and devotion: Jesus Christ. Throughout our 500-year history as Anabaptists—through trial, oppression, emigration, schism and change—our model for living has always been found in the way of Jesus. Since Jesus is so central to our journey, it is appropriate that we devote this volume of songs and worship resources to the One who embodies the heart of God.

Appropriate for any time of the year, *Sing the Story* uses the seasons of the church year from Advent to Pentecost to proclaim the life, ministry, death, resurrection, and reign of Jesus through song and word. In a refreshing array of new and old texts, rich imagery, varied languages and ethnic styles, unison and four-part harmonies—Jesus Christ emerges as the character and passion of God, the Light of the World, and the Bringer of Good News. These songs and worship resources also emphasize our growing unity in the worldwide church, strengthening and broadening our connections and relationships with Christian sisters and brothers everywhere.

This volume tells the *story* of Jesus, and every good story has a beginning, a middle, and an end. We have chosen, therefore, to order this volume's contents beginning with the advent of Christ, and ending with Christ's return and ultimate reign over all creation. In doing so, we hope that a clear and consistent story will emerge of Jesus as the revelation of God, the One who ultimately points us to God. For additional help in navigating this volume, we have included a convenient index at the back, organized by acts of worship, similar to *Hymnal: A Worship Book* and *Sing the Journey*.

In every age, the message of Jesus competes with the world's message. In the 21st century, nationalism, high-tech warfare, terrorism, apathy toward environmental concerns, genocide, racism, sexism, over-consumption, and greed oppose the voice of Christ. In these songs and texts, may the community of faith find a common voice that rises above that of the world and sings together:

*My heart shall sing of the day you bring. Let the fires of your justice burn.
Wipe away all tears, for the dawn draws near, and the world is about to turn! (#124)*

To the glory of God.

—Randall Spaulding

Members of the *Hymnal* supplement committee:
Randall Spaulding, Kenneth J. Nafziger, Marlene Kropf, Jeff Enns, James E. Clemens, Carmen Horst, Marilyn Houser Hamm

TABLE OF CONTENTS

Introduction .... *iii*

ADVENT: Prepare the Way 1-16

CHRISTMAS: Celebrate New Birth 17-28

EPIPHANY: Welcome the Light 29-34

MINISTRY OF JESUS: Follow the Way 35-57

LENT: Journey to the Cross 58-72

HOLY WEEK: Behold the Lamb 73-86

EASTER: Rise to New Life 87-101

PENTECOST: Receive the Spirit 102-107

REIGN OF CHRIST: Watch for God Among Us 108-124

WORSHIP RESOURCES 125-204

Index of Copyright Holders for Hymns .... page 197
Addresses of Copyright Holders for Hymns .... page 199
Index of Copyright Holders for Worship Resources .... page 200
First Line Index of Hymns .... page 202
Acts of Worship Index for Hymns .... page 205
Acts of Worship Index for Worship Resources .... page 207

Praise the One who breaks the darkness 1

NETTLETON 87. 87D

1 Praise the One who breaks the dark-ness with a   lib - er - at-ing light;
2 Praise the One who blessed the chil-dren with a strong yet gen-tle word;
3 Praise the One true love in - car-nate: Christ, who suf-fered in our place;

praise the One who frees the pris-'ners, turn-ing blind-ness in - to sight.
praise the One who drove out de-mons with a pierc-ing, two-edged sword.
Je - sus died and rose for man - y that we may know God by grace.

Praise the One who preached the gos - pel, heal-ing ev-'ry dread dis -ease,
Praise the One who brings cool wa - ter to the des-ert's burn-ing sand;
Let   us   sing for   joy   and glad-ness, see-ing what our God has done.

calm - ing storms and feed-ing thou-sands with the ver - y bread of peace.
from this   well comes liv-ing wa - ter quench-ing thirst in ev - 'ry land.
Praise the   one re-deem-ing glo-ry; praise the One who makes us one.

Text: Rusty Edwards
Music: American folk melody, J. Wyeth's *Repository of Sacred Music, Part Second*, 1813

2

Maranatha, come

MARANATHA, COME Irregular with refrain

Refrain

Ma-ra-na-tha, come, come, Lord Je-sus.

Ma-ra-na-tha, come, come, Lord Je-sus.

Ma-ra-na-tha, come, come, O God.

Ma-ra-na-tha, come, come, O God.

To verses   Final

Verses

1 Wis - dom of God, guid - ing cre - a - tion,
2 O sa - cred Lord, come in your glo - ry;
3 From Jes - se's stem raise up your peo - ple.
4 O roy - al pow'r, O key of Dav - id,
5 O ra - diant dawn, O sun of jus - tice,

6 Rul - er of all, joy of our long - ing,
7 Sav - ior of all, hope of the na - tions,

Text: Francis Patrick O'Brien, based on the "O" Antiphons
Music: Francis Patrick O'Brien
Text and Music copyright © 1996 GIA Publications, Inc.

D.C.

1 lead us in ways that are faith - ful to your name.
2 stretch forth your hand____ and we____ shall be free.

3 Let noth - ing keep you from com - ing to our aid.
4 o - pen the heav - ens and lead us in - to life.
5 shine on your peo - ple in dark-ness and in death.

6 come save the peo - ple you fash - ion from the dust.
7 bring us to free - dom, E - man - u - el

Come, Light of the world

LIGHT OF THE WORLD 55. 55

3

Come, Light of the world.   Come, Light of the world!

Come, Light of the world.   Come, Light of the world!

Additional text:
Come, Spirit of God …
Come, Prince of Peace …
Christ, hear our prayer …

Text: traditional
Music: Randall L. Spaulding, 2002

4 Rejoice, rejoice, the Savior comes

ST. MARTIN'S CM

1 Re - joice, re - joice, the Sav - ior comes, the Sav - ior prom - ised long; let ev - 'ry heart pre - pare a throne and ev - 'ry voice a song.

2 He comes the pris - 'ners to re - lease, in e - vil bond - age held. The gates of brass be - fore him burst, the i - ron fet - ters yield.

3 He comes the bro - ken heart to bind, the bleed - ing soul to cure, and with the trea - sures of God's grace to bless the hum - ble poor.

4 Our glad ho - san - nas, Prince of Peace, your wel - come shall pro - claim, and heav'n's e - ter - nal arch - es ring with your be - lov - ed name.

Text: James Montgomery (1771-1854), alt.
Music: William Tans'ur, c. 1755

Open my ears, open my eyes   5

INVOCATION Irregular

Text: James E. Clemens, 2005, *A Field of Voices,* 2007
Music: James E. Clemens, 2005, *A Field of Voices,* 2007

Prepare the Way

6 Save us, O Lord

SAVE US, O LORD Irregular with refrain

Refrain

Save us, O Lord; car-ry us back. Rouse your pow-er and come.

Res-cue your peo-ple; show us your face. Bring us back.

Verse 1

1 O Shep-herd of Is-ra-el, hear us. Re-turn and we shall be saved. A-rise, O Lord; hear our cries, O Lord: bring us back! *To refrain*

Verse 2

2 How long will you hide from your peo-ple? We long to see your face. Give ear to us. Draw near to us, Lord God of hosts! *To refrain*

Verse 3

3 Turn a-gain; care for your vine; pro-tect what your right hand has plant-ed. Your vine-yards are tram-pled, up-root-ed, and burned. Come to us, Fa-ther of might! *To refrain*

Text: Bob Dufford, SJ, based on Psalm 80
Music: Bob Dufford, SJ

Come, come Emmanuel

7

ADVENT GATHERING SONG* Irregular

*Original title

Text: James J. Chepponis
Music: James J. Chepponis
Text and Music copyright © 1995 GIA Publications, Inc.

8 Wild and lone the prophet's voice

LA GRANGE 77. 77D

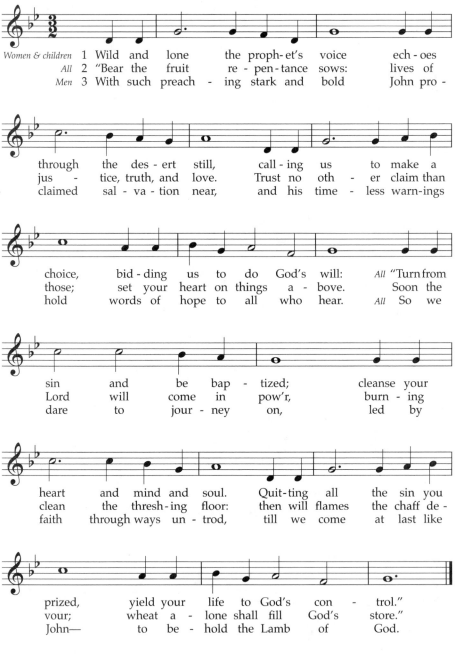

Women & children 1 Wild and lone the proph-et's voice ech-oes
All 2 "Bear the fruit re - pen-tance sows: lives of
Men 3 With such preach - ing stark and bold John pro -

through the des - ert still, call - ing us to make a
jus - tice, truth, and love. Trust no oth - er claim than
claimed sal - va - tion near, and his time - less warn-ings

choice, bid - ding us to do God's will: All "Turn from
those; set your heart on things a - bove. Soon the
hold words of hope to all who hear. All So we

sin and be bap - tized; cleanse your
Lord will come in pow'r, burn - ing
dare to jour - ney on, led by

heart and mind and soul. Quit-ting all the sin you
clean the thresh-ing floor: then will flames the chaff de -
faith through ways un - trod, till we come at last like

prized, yield your life to God's con - trol."
vour; wheat a - lone shall fill God's store."
John— to be - hold the Lamb of God.

Text: Carl P. Daw, Jr., based on Matthew 3; Mark 1:1-11; Luke 3:1-22; John 1:19-37
Music: David Ashley White

As the pauper waits for plenty 9

BRIDEGROOM 87. 87. 6

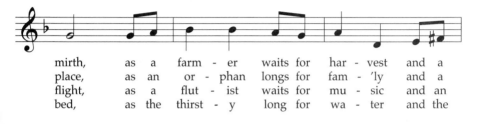

1 As the pau - per waits for plen - ty, as the weep-ing wait for
2 As the blos - som longs for spring-time and the seed, a fer - tile
3 As a song-bird waits for morn - ing and an ea - glet waits for
4 As the home-less long for shel - ter and the wea - ry, for a

mirth, as a farm - er waits for har - vest and a
place, as an or - phan longs for fam - 'ly and a
flight, as a flut - ist waits for mu - sic and an
bed, as the thirst - y long for wa - ter and the

1-3

wom-an waits for birth, so do I wait for you.
child, his moth-er's face, so do I long for you.
art - ist waits for light, so do I wait for you.
hun - gry long for bread, so do I long for

4

you. So do you long for me.

10 Come! Walk in the light

COME! WALK IN THE LIGHT Irregular with refrain

Come! Walk in the light. Come! walk in the light of day.

Come! Walk in the light. Come! walk in the light of day.

1 In the days ahead, the nations will stream to the house of the Holy One.
Many peoples will turn to God. They will learn God's ways and walk in God's light.

2 And God will judge every nation and tribe. They will beat their swords into plows,
and their spears into pruning hooks. Never shall they practice war anymore.

3 The wolf and the lamb will live together. The cattle will graze with the bear;
their young will lie down together. On God's holy mountain will there be peace.

4 Let the mountains be laden with God's peace, and the hills be filled with justice.
Like showers that water the earth, let God's light rain on the valleys and fields.

5 O God, Lord of Hosts, how long? How long, O Lord, will you be angry with our prayers,
will you feed us the bread of our tears? Restore us. Let us walk again in your light.

6 Lift your eyes. Arise. Shine. Your light has come. Now you will see and be radiant.
The brightness of the dawn is here. God makes the way clear. Come, walk in the light.

Alternate Refrain (unaccompanied)

Text: Advent 2004 Committee (refrain), 2003; David Wright (verses), 2005, *A Field of Voices,* 2007
Verses copyright © 2005 David Wright
Music: James E. Clemens, 2003, 2005, *A Field of Voices,* 2007
Copyright © 2003, 2005 James E. Clemens

No wind at the window

11

COLUMCILLE 11 11. 11 11

1 No wind at the win-dow, no knock on the door; no
2 "O Ma - ry, O Ma - ry, don't hide from my face. Be
3 "This child must be born that the king-dom might come: sal -
4 No pay-ment was prom-ised, no prom - is - es made; no

light from the lamp-stand, no foot on the floor; no
glad that you're fa - vored and filled with God's grace. The
va - tion for man - y, de - struc-tion for some; both
wed-ding was dat - ed, no blue-print dis - played. Yet

dream born of tired-ness, no ghost raised by fear: just an
time for re - deem-ing the world has be - gun; and
end and be - gin-ning, both mes - sage and sign; both
Ma - ry, con - sent-ing to what none could guess, re -

an - gel and a wom - an and a voice in her ear.
you are re - quest - ed to moth - er God's Son."
vic - tor and vic - tim, both yours and di - vine."
plied with con - vic - tion, "Tell God I say, 'Yes.'"

Text: John L. Bell
Copyright © 1992 WGRG The Iona Community (Scotland). Used by permission of GIA Publications, Inc., exclusive agent.
Music: Irish traditional; arranged by Marty Haugen
Arrangement copyright © 1995 GIA Publications, Inc.

12 Magnificat

MAGNIFICAT

Ma-gni-fi-cat, Ma-gni-fi-cat, Ma-gni-fi-cat a-ni-ma me-a Do-mi-num.*

Ma - gni-fi-cat, Ma - gni-fi-cat, Ma-gni-fi-cat a-ni-ma me - a!

Secondary Canon *(or unison choir with trumpet)*

Ma - gni - fi - cat, Ma - gni - fi - cat, a - ni-ma me-a Do - mi-num, a - ni-ma me-a Do - mi-num.

Choir

Ma - gni - fi - cat, Ma - gni - fi - cat a - ni - ma me - a, me - a Do - mi - num.

*Translation: My soul magnifies the Lord.

Text: Taizé Community, Luke 1:46, 1978
Music: Jacques Berthier (1923-1994)

Sing we a song of high revolt   13

DEO GRACIAS LM

1 Sing we a song of high re - volt; make great the
2 Sing we of God who deep - ly cares and still with
3 By God the poor are lift - ed up; God sat - is -
4 God calls us to re - volt and trust, to work for

Lord, God's name ex - ult! Sing we the words of
us our bur - den shares. God, who with strength the
fies with bread and cup the hun - gry folk of
what is right and just, to catch the vi - sion

Ma - ry's song of God at war with hu-man wrong.
proud dis - owns, brings down the might - y from their thrones.
man - y lands; the rich are left with emp-ty hands.
Ma - ry caught, to sing and live Mag - ni - fi - cat.

For accompaniment ideas, see number 236 in *Hymnal Accompaniment Handbook*.

Text: Fred Kaan; verse 4 adapted by Carmen Horst
   Copyright © 1968 Hope Publishing Company, Carol Stream, IL 60188. All rights reserved. Used by permission.
Music: English melody, 15th c.

Prepare the way of the Lord   14

Canon   PREPARE THE WAY

Pre - pare the way of the Lord. Pre - pare the way of the Lord, and

all peo-ple will see the sal - va - tion of our God. Pre -

Secondary Canon

Al - le-lu - ia. Al - le-lu - ia. Al - le -

lu - ia. Al - le - lu - ia.

Text: Taizé Community, Luke 3:4,6, 1984
Music: Jacques Berthier
   Text and Music copyright © 1984 Les Presses de Taizé (France). Used by permission of GIA Publications, Inc.

15 Hope is a candle

GALLOWAY TAM 11 10. 11 8

1 Hope is a can - dle, once lit by the proph - ets,
2 Peace is a can - dle to show us a path - way,
3 Love is a can - dle whose light makes a cir - cle,
4 Joy is a can - dle of mys - t'ry and laugh - ter,
5 Christ is the light that the proph - ets a - wait - ed,

1 nev - er con - sumed, though it burns through the years;
2 threat - ened by gusts from our rage and our greed.
3 where ev - 'ry face is the face of a friend.
4 mys - t'ry of light that is born in the dark;
5 Christ is the li - on, the lamb, and the child.

1 dim in the day - light of pow - er and priv - i - lege—
2 Friend, feel no en - vy for those in the shad - ows—
3 Wid - en the cir - cle by shar - ing and giv - ing—
4 laugh - ter at hear - ing the voice of an an - gel,
5 Christ is the love and the mys - t'ry and laugh - ter—

1 when they are gone, hope will shine on.
2 vio - lence and force their dead - end course.
3 God's ho - ly dare: love ev - ery - where.
4 ev - er so near, cast - ing out fear.
5 can - dles, make way! Christ is the day.

Text: Richard Leach, 1994
Music: Scottish folk melody

Peace before us

16

PRAYER OF PEACE 445.447

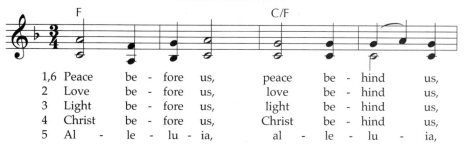

1,6	Peace	be - fore us,	peace	be - hind	us,
2	Love	be - fore us,	love	be - hind	us,
3	Light	be - fore us,	light	be - hind	us,
4	Christ	be - fore us,	Christ	be - hind	us,
5	Al - le - lu - ia,	al - le - lu - ia,

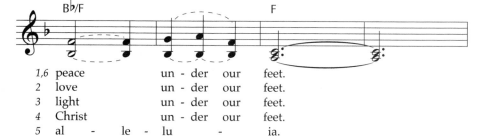

1,6 peace un - der our feet.
2 love un - der our feet.
3 light un - der our feet.
4 Christ un - der our feet.
5 al - le - lu - ia.

1,6 Peace with - in us, peace o - ver us,
2 Love with - in us, love o - ver us,
3 Light with - in us, light o - ver us,
4 Christ with - in us, Christ o - ver us,
5 Al - le - lu - ia, al - le - lu - ia,

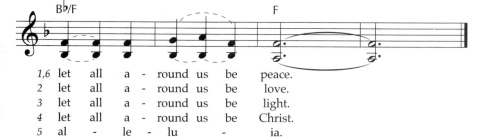

1,6 let all a - round us be peace.
2 let all a - round us be love.
3 let all a - round us be light.
4 let all a - round us be Christ.
5 al - le - lu - ia.

Text: David Haas, based on a Navajo prayer
Music: David Haas
Text and Music copyright © 1987 GIA Publications, Inc.

17 Alleluia!

Al - le - lu - ia! Al - le - lu - ia!

Al - le - lu - ia! Al - le - lu - ia!

Music: Norah Duncan IV

18 Erfreue dich (Be joyful)

55. 55 with refrain

German: 1 Er - freu - e dich, Him - mel, er - freu - e dich, Er - de;
2 Ihr Son - nen und Mon - de, ihr fun - keln-den Ster - ne,
English: 1 Be joy - ful, oh heav - ens, be joy - ful, oh earth.
2 Bright sun and soft moon-beams, oh glit - ter - ing star-light,

er - freu - e sich al - les, was fröh - lich kann wer - den.
ihr Räu - me des Alls in un - end - li - cher Fern - ne:
Be joy - ful, all na - ture that joy - ful can be.
you vast spa - cious un - i - verse, heav - ens e - ter - nal:

Text: Straßburg 1697 (v. 1 & 6); Maria Luise Thurmair-Mumelter, 1963 (v. 2–5); tr. Jean Janzen, 2006
Translation copyright © 2006 Jean Janzen
Music: Augsburg 1659 / Bamberg 1691

Refrain

Auf Er - den hier un - ten, im Him - mel dort o - ben:
On earth here be - low us, in heav - en a - bove us,

Den gü - ti - gen va - ter, den wol - len wir lo - ben.
Cre - a - tor, all gra - cious, we hon - or and praise you.

GERMAN

3 Ihr Tiefen des Meeres,
Gelaich und Gewürme,
Schnee, Hagel und Regen,
ihr brausenden Stürme:
Refrain

4 Ihr Wüsten und Weiden,
Gebirg und Geklüfte,
ihr Tiere des Feldes,
ihr Vögel der Lüfte:
Refrain

5 Ihr Männer und Frauen,
ihr Kinder und Greise,
ihr Kleinen und Großen,
einfältig und weise:
Refrain

6 Erd, Wasser, Luft, Feuer
und himmlische Flammen,
ihr Menschen und Engel,
stimmt alle zusammen:
Refrain

ENGLISH

3 You depths of the ocean,
all fish and sea creatures,
snow, hailstones, and raindrops,
you storms with your raging:
Refrain

4 You deserts and meadows,
all mountains and valleys,
all animals grazing,
birds singing and winging:
Refrain

5 All men and all women,
you children and aged,
the small and the tall ones,
you simple and wise ones:
Refrain

6 Earth, water, air, fire,
you bright, flaming heavens,
all people and angels,
sing harmony ever:
Refrain

19

Jesus, Jesus, oh, what a wonderful child

WONDERFUL CHILD 11 10. 89. 11

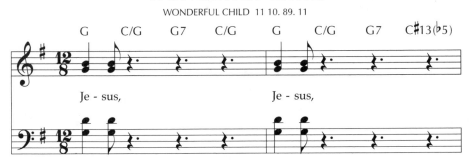

Je - sus,   Je - sus,

oh,   what a won-der-ful Child.

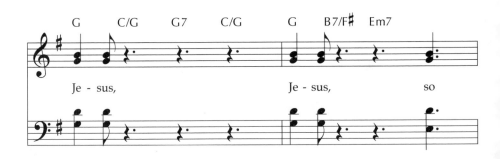

Je - sus,   Je - sus,   so

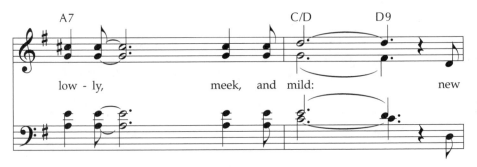

low - ly,   meek, and mild: new

Text: traditional spiritual
Music: traditional spiritual; arranged by Mark Hayes, 1999

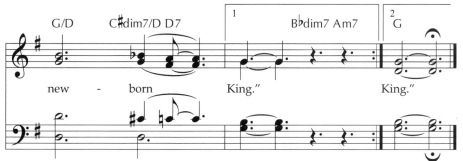

20 Hacia Belén se en caminan
(Walking slowly unto Bethl'em)

ALEGRÍA* 88. 88 with refrain

Spanish: 1 Ha - cia Be - lén se en-ca - mi - nan Ma - ría
(2 En cuan) - to a Be - lén lle - ga - ron po - sa -
English: 1 Walk - ing slow - ly un - to Beth-l'em, ho - ly
(2 When to) Beth - l'em they had trav - eled, they were

con su a - man-te es - po - so, lle-van-do en su com - pa -
da al pun - to pi - die-ron; na-die les qui - so hos-pe -
Ma - ry, with her hus-band; trav-'ling with them though in
search-ing for a ha - ven; all the inn-keep - ers re -

ñí - a a to - do un Dios po - de - ro - so.
dar____ por - que tan po - bres les vie-ron.
se - cret, is the Sav - ior of all na-tions.
fused them, dressed so poor and heav - y lad - en.

Refrain

¡A - le - grí-a, a - le-grí-a, a - le - grí - a, a - le -

grí-a, a - le-grí-a y pla - cer!** Que la Vir-gen va de
For the vir - gin pass - es

pa - so con su es - po - so ha - cia Be - lén. ¡A - le -
by us with her hus-band un - to Beth-l'em.

*Original title

**Translation: Joy and pleasure.

Text: Puerto Rican traditional
Music: Puerto Rican traditional; arranged by Conrad Susa
Arrangement copyright © E.C. Schirmer

grí-a, a-le-grí-a, a-le - grí-a, a-le - grí-a, a-le-grí-a, y pla -

¡A - le - grí - a, a - le - grí - a, y pla -

cer! Que la Vir-gen va de pa-so con su es-
For the vir-gin pass-es by us with her

cer! Que la Vir-gen va de pa-so con su es -
For the vir-gin pass-es by us with her

po-so ha - cia Be - lén.
hus-band to Beth-le - hem.

2 En cuan-
2 When to

po-so ha - cia Be - lén.
hus-band to Beth-le - hem.

lén.
hem.

3 Los pa - ja - ri - llos del
3 As they see Ma - ry and

lén.
hem.

bos-que a ver pa - sar los es - po-sos les can-
Jo - seph, all the song-birds of the for-est ser - e -

Celebrate New Birth

ta - ban me - lo - dí - as con sus tri - nos ar - mo - nio - sos.
nade them with their sing-ing; pre-cious gifts come from the poor-est.

Final refrain

¡A - le - grí - a, a - le - grí - a, a - le - grí - a, a - le -

grí - a, a - le - grí - a, y pla - cer! Que la Vir - gen va de
For the vir - gin pass - es

pa - so con su es - po - so ha - cia Be - lén. ¡A - le -
by us with her hus-band un - to Beth-l'em.

grí - a, a - le - grí - a, a - le - grí - a, y pla -

¡A - le - grí - a, a - le - grí - a, a - le - grí - a, y pla -

cer! Que la Vir - gen va de pa - so con su es -
For the vir - gin pass - es by us with her

cer!

po - so ha - cia Be - lén.
hus - band to Beth - le - hem.

Sing we the virgin Mary

21

SING WE THE VIRGIN MARY Irregular

1   Sing we the vir - gin Ma - ry, sing
2 So si - lent - ly came our Je - sus un -
3 When Je - sus was a - born - ing, to
4 Ah, bless - ed maid - en moth - er, be -

we that match - less one; see how the an - gels at -
to his sweet Ma - ry, as dew of A - pril
earth came heav - en down, to lie up - on a
known to proph - e - cy: now Je - sus is a -

tend - ed her when she birth - ed God's own
fall - eth on flower so ten - der -
man - ger, a - way in Beth - lem's
born - ed, and all will hon - or

Son, when she birth - ed God's own Son.
ly, on flower so ten - der - ly.
town, a - way in Beth - lem's town.
thee, and all will hon - or thee.

Text: Appalachian traditional(?), John Jacob Niles, 1945-7
Music: Appalachian traditional(?), John Jacob Niles, 1945-7

22 There were angels hov'ring round

ANGELS HOVERING ROUND 779

1 There were an - gels hov - 'ring round, there were
2 They___ sing in har - mo - ny, they___
3 The___ child___ in her arms, the___
4 The___ shep - herds on their knees, the___
5 There are an - gels hov - 'ring round, there are

1 an - gels hov - 'ring round, there were an - gels,
2 sing in har - mo - ny, they___ sing, they
3 child___ in her arms, the___ child, the
4 shep - herds on their knees, the___ shep - herds,
5 an - gels hov - 'ring round, there are an - gels,

1 an - gels hov - 'ring round!
2 sing in har - mo - ny.
3 child___ in her arms.
4 shep - herds on their knees.
5 an - gels hov - 'ring round!

More verses may be added to fill out the story.

Text: American folk hymn
Music: American folk hymn

Gloria, gloria, gloria

23

GLORIA CUECA Irregular

Spanish: ¡Glo - ria, glo - ria, glo - ria   en   las al - tur - as   a   Dios!
English: *Glo - ria, glo - ria, glo - ria,*   *glo - ry to God___ on   high!*

Y en la tie - rra paz pa-ra a-qué-llos__ que a - ma el Se - ñor.
And   on earth___ peace to all peo-ple in whom God is well   pleased.

Accompaniment patterns

Congas

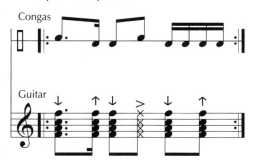

Guitar

Text: Luke 2:14
Music: Pablo Sosa

24 Alleluia

JOYFUL ALLELUIA*

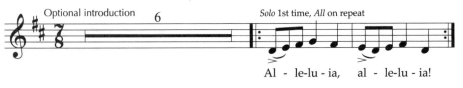

Al - le-lu - ia, al - le-lu - ia!

Al - le-lu - ia, al - le-lu - ia!   Al - le-lu - ia, al - le-lu - ia!

Al - le-lu - ia, al - le-lu - ia!

*Original title

Music: Howard Hughes, S.M.
Copyright © 1973, 1979 GIA Publications, Inc.

A stable lamp is lighted

25

ANDUJAR 76. 76. 66. 76

1 A sta - ble lamp is light - ed whose
2 This child through Da - vid's cit - y shall
3 Yet he shall be for - sak - en, and
4 But now, as at the end - ing, the

glow shall wake the sky; the stars shall bend their
ride in tri - umph by; the palm shall strew its
yield - ed up to die; the sky shall groan and
low is lift - ed high; the stars shall bend their

voic - es, and ev - 'ry stone shall cry.
branch - es, and ev - 'ry stone shall cry.
dark - en, and ev - 'ry stone shall cry.
voic - es, and ev - 'ry stone shall cry.

And ev - 'ry stone shall cry, and
And ev - 'ry stone shall cry, though
And ev - 'ry stone shall cry, in
And ev - 'ry stone shall cry, in

straw like gold shall shine; a barn shall har - bor
heav - y, dull, and dumb, and lie with - in the
hearts made hard by sin: God's blood up - on the
prais - es of the child by whose de - scent a -

heav - en, a stall be - come a shrine.
road - way to pave his king - dom come.
spear - head, God's love re - fused a - gain.
mong us the worlds are rec - on - ciled.

Text: Richard Wilbur
Copyright © 1961 Richard Wilbur
Music: David Hurd
Copyright © 1984 GIA Publications, Inc.

26 Helpless and hungry

CHILD OF THE POOR* 548. 585 with refrain

1 Help-less and hun-gry, low-ly, a-fraid, wrapped in the
2 Who is the strang-er here in our midst, look-ing for
3 Bring all the thirst-y, all who seek peace; bring those with

chill of mid-win-ter; comes now a-mong us, born in-to
shel-ter a-mong us? Who is the out-cast? Who do we
noth-ing to of-fer. Strength-en the fee-ble, say to the

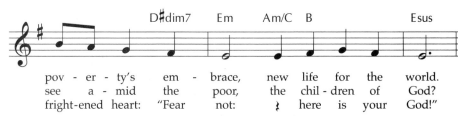

pov-er-ty's em-brace, new life for the world.
see a-mid the poor, the chil-dren of God?
fright-ened heart: "Fear not: here is your God!"

Refrain

Who is this who lives with the low-ly, shar-ing their sor-rows,

know-ing their hun-ger? This is Christ, re-vealed to the world in the

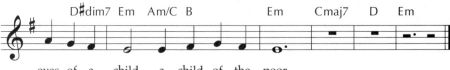

eyes of a child, a child of the poor.

*Original title

This hymn may be sung with *What child is this* (*Hymnal: A Worship Book* #215, melody only) as follows:
Helpless and hungry, v. 1, followed by *What child is this*, v. 1;
Helpless and hungry, v. 2, followed by *What child is this*, v. 2;
both sung simultaneously on v. 3.

Text: Scott Soper
Music: Scott Soper

Sing a different song

DIFFERENT SONG 10 10. 66. 10

1 Sing a dif-ferent song now
2 Shout a dif-ferent shout now
3 Love a dif-ferent love now
4 Dance a dif-ferent dance now

Christ-mas is here, sing a song of peo - ple know - ing God's
Christ-mas is here, shout a shout of joy and gen - u - ine
Christ-mas is here, love with-out con - di - tion, love with-out
Christ-mas is here, dance a dance of war on suf - fering and

near: The Mes - si - ah is born in the
cheer: Fill the earth and the sky with the
fear: With the hum - ble and poor, with the
fear: Peace and jus - tice are one, in the

face of our scorn, sing a dif-ferent song to wel-come and
news from on high, shout a dif-ferent shout that all may come
shy and un - sure, love a dif-ferent love. Let Christ be the
light of the sun. Dance a dif-ferent dance. God's reign has be -

warn.
by.
cure!
gun!

Text: The Iona Community, 1987, based on Isaiah 9:2, 6–7; 42:10–11; Matthew 1:23, alt.
Music: John L. Bell, 1987

28 Holy Child within the manger

JOYOUS LIGHT 87. 87D

1 Ho - ly Child with-in the man-ger, long a - go, yet ev-er near;
2 Once a - gain we tell the sto - ry—how your love for us was shown,
3 Ho - ly Child with-in the man-ger, lead us ev - er in your way,

come as friend to ev-'ry stran-ger, come as hope for ev-'ry fear.
when the Im - age of your glo - ry wore an im-age like our own.
so we see in ev-'ry stran-ger how you come to us to - day.

As you lived to heal the bro-ken, greet the out-cast, free the bound,
Come, en - light-en with your wis-dom, come and fill us with your grace,
In our lives and in our liv - ing give us strength to live as you,

as you taught us love un-spo-ken, teach us now where you are found.
may the fire of your com-pas-sion kin-dle ev-'ry land and race.
that our hearts might be for-giv - ing and our spir-its strong and true.

Text: Marty Haugen
Music: Marty Haugen
Text and Music copyright © 1987 GIA Publications, Inc.

Brightest and best

29

MORNING STAR 11 10. 11 10

1,5 Bright - est and best of the stars of the morn - ing,
2 Cold on his cra - dle the dew - drops are shin - ing,
3 Shall we not yield him, in cost - ly de - vo - tion,
4 Vain - ly we of - fer each am - ple ob - la - tion,

dawn on our dark - ness, and lend us your aid.
low lies his head with the beasts of the stall.
fra - grance of E - dom and of - f'rings di - vine,
vain - ly with gifts would his fa - vor se - cure.

Star of the East, the ho - ri - zon a - dorn - ing,
An - gels a - dore him in slum - ber re - clin - ing.
gems of the moun - tain and pearls of the o - cean,
Rich - er by far is the heart's ad - o - ra - tion,

guide where our in - fant re - deem - er is laid.
Mak - er, and Mon - arch, and Sav - ior of all.
myrrh from the for - est, or gold from the mine?
dear - er to God are the prayers of the poor.

Text: Reginald Heber, *Christian Observer*, 1811, alt.
Music: James P. Harding, *The Church Hymnal*, 1892

30 Arise, your light is come!

FESTAL SONG SM

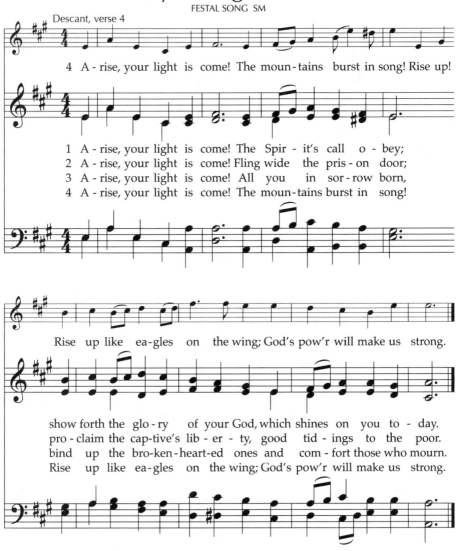

Descant, verse 4

4 A-rise, your light is come! The moun-tains burst in song! Rise up!

1 A - rise, your light is come! The Spir - it's call o - bey;
2 A - rise, your light is come! Fling wide the pris - on door;
3 A - rise, your light is come! All you in sor - row born,
4 A - rise, your light is come! The moun-tains burst in song!

Rise up like ea-gles on the wing; God's pow'r will make us strong.

show forth the glo - ry of your God, which shines on you to - day.
pro - claim the cap-tive's lib - er - ty, good tid - ings to the poor.
bind up the bro-ken-heart-ed ones and com - fort those who mourn.
Rise up like ea-gles on the wing; God's pow'r will make us strong.

Text: Ruth Duck, 1974
Copyright © 1992 GIA Publications, Inc.
Music: William Henry Walter, 1894; descant by Diana McLeod, 1995
Descant copyright © 1995 Diana McLeod

Jesus, be the center

31

BE THE CENTRE* Irregular

1 Je - sus, be the cen - ter, be my source, be my light, Je - sus.

2 Je - sus, be the cen - ter. Be my hope, be my song, Je - sus. Be the fi -

3 Je - sus, be my vi - sion. Be my path, be my guide, Je - sus.

re in my heart. Be the wind in these sails. Be the rea -

son that I live, Je - sus, Je - sus.

4 Je - sus, be the cen - ter, be my source, be my light, Je - sus. Je - sus.

*Original title

Text: Michael Frye
Music: Michael Frye
Text and Music copyright © 1999 Vineyard Songs (UK/Eire) (PRS); admin. North America by Music Services

32 Oh, beautiful star of Bethlehem

BEAUTIFUL STAR OF BETHLEHEM 98 10. 98 10 with refrain

1 Oh, beau - ti - ful star of Beth - le - hem, shin-ing a -
2 Oh, beau - ti - ful star, the hope of light, guid-ing the
3 Oh, beau - ti - ful star, the hope of rest, for the re -

far thro' shad - ows dim, giv-ing a light for those who long have
pil - grim thro' the night, o - ver the moun-tain till the break of
deemed, the good and blest, yon-der in glo - ry when the crown is

gone, (have gone,) and guid-ing the wise men on their way
dawn; (the dawn;) and in - to the light of per - fect day
won; (is won,) for Je - sus is now that Star di - vine;

un - to the place where Je - sus lay,
it will give out a love - ly ray; beau - ti - ful
bright - er and bright - er he will shine;

Text: Adger M. Pace, 1940
Music: R. Fisher Boyce, 1940; harmonized by Adger M. Pace

33 Let justice roll like a river

LET JUSTICE ROLL Irregular with refrain

Text: Marty Haugen, based on Amos 5:21-24, 8;4; Micah 4:3-4, 6;8; Joel 2:12-14
Music: Marty Haugen

Verse 1

1 Take from me your ho- ly feasts, all your of - f'rings
and your mu- sic; let jus - tice flow like
wa - ters, and in - teg - ri - ty like an
ev - er-flow - ing stream.

Verses 2–5

2 How long shall we wait, O God, for the
3 Hear this, all of you who use the poor in your
4 E - ven now re - turn to me, let your
5 You have been told the way of life, the

2 day of your mer - cy to dawn, the
3 thirst of pow - er and rich - es: the
4 hearts be bro - ken and hum - ble, for
5 way of jus - tice and peace; to

Welcome the Light

2 day   we   beat   our   swords in - to   ploughs,   when your

3 Lord   will   turn   your   laugh-ter   to   tears,   on   the
4 I   am   gra - cious,   gen-'rous and   kind;   come and

5 act   just - ly,   to   love   gent - ly,   and

2 peace   reigns   o - ver   the   earth?

3 won - drous   Day   of   our   God.
4 seek   the   mer - cies   of   God.

5 walk   hum - bly   with   God.

You are holy

DU ÄR HELIG Irregular

34

Part 1

You are ho - ly, you are whole. You are
are you com - ing near. Bless - ed

al - ways ev - er more than we ev - er un - der - stand.
are you com - ing here to your church in wine and bread,

You are al - ways at hand. Bless-ed
raised from soil, raised from dead.

Part 2

You are ho - ly, you are whole-ness, you are
lu - jah, hal - le - lu - jah, hal - le -

pres - ent, let the cos - mos praise you Lord!
lu - jah, hal - le -

Hal - le - lu - jah. A - men.

FRENCH

Tu es saint et abondance, et tu es toute puissance,
plus que nous ne comprenons. En toi nous nous confions.
Bénis ton prochain retour, en nos âmes ton labour.
Pour ton peuple le pain, le vin de la terre cadeau divin.

Tu es saint, plénitude, tu es présent,
  que l'univers te loue Seigneur.
Alléluia, alléluia, alléluia, alléluia, Seigneur.

SPANISH

Eres santo, eres Dios por toda la eternidad;
siempre tu muy cerca estás de tu pueblo, buen Señor.
Te alabamos hoy aquí, te adoramos con fervor.
A tu iglesia en vino y pan nueva vida así le das.

Eres santo, eres Dios, te sentimos.
  La creación te dé loor.
Aleluya, aleluya, aleluya, aleluya, Señor.

Parts 1 and 2 can be sung at the same time.

Text: Per Harling, alt.
Music: Per Harling
  Text and Music copyright © Oxford University Press

35 Thou, O Christ, my Lord and King

IN ME 77. 77D

1 Thou, O Christ, my Lord and King, grant in thine own
2 Thou a won-der work-ing God, dwell-ing in e-
3 Prince of peace be-yond com-pare, thou whose pow-er

4 O thou might-y God of love, died thy-self to
5 Je-sus, thou the life, the way, in thine im-age
6 Je-sus, thou the joy un-told, like a riv-er

1 name my plea. Take the sac-ri-fice I bring,
2 ter-ni-ty, as in flesh our plan-et trod,
3 stilled the sea, chief a-mong ten thou-sand-fair,

4 set us free. Ho-ly Spir-it, heav'n-ly dove,
5 let me be; keep my heart from day to day,
6 flow-ing free. Be thou ev-er in my soul,

1 be thou "all thou art" in me. Be thou "all thou
2 work thy might-y work in me. Work thy might-y
3 speak thy word of peace in me. Speak thy word of

4 mag-ni-fy thy love in me. Mag-ni-fy thy
5 live thy ho-ly life in me. Live thy ho-ly
6 let thy joy a-bound in me. Let thy joy a-

Text: Charles A. Tindley
Music: Charles A. Tindley; arranged by Frederick J. Tindley

36 Jesus, tempted in the desert

EBENEZER 87. 87D

1 Je - sus, tempt - ed in the des - ert,
2 Je - sus, tempt - ed at the tem - ple,
3 Je - sus, tempt - ed on the moun - tain
4 When we face temp - ta - tion's pow - er,

lone - ly, hun - gry, filled with dread: "Use your pow'r," the
high a - bove its an - cient wall: "Throw your - self from
by the lure of vast do - main: "Fall be - fore me!
lone - ly strug - gling, filled with dread, Christ, who knew the

tempt - er tells him; "turn these bar - ren rock to bread!"
loft - y tur - ret; an - gels wait to break your fall!"
Be my ser - vant! Glo - ry, fame, you're sure to gain!"
tempt - er's ho - ur, come and be our liv - ing bread.

Text: Herman G. Stuempfle, Jr.
Copyright © 1993 GIA Publications, Inc.
Music: Thomas J. Williams, 1896, *Baptist Book of Praise*, 1901

"Not a - lone by bread," he an-swers, "can the hu-man
Je - sus shuns such emp - ty mar-vels, feats that fick - le
Je - sus sees the daz-zling vi - sion, turns his eyes an -
By your grace, pro - tect, pre - serve us lest we fall, your

heart be filled. On - ly by the Word that calls us
crowds re - quest: "God, whose grace pro - tects, pre - serves us,
oth - er way: "God a - lone de - serves our hom - age!
trust be - tray. Yours, a - bove all oth - er voice - es,

is our deep - est hun - ger stilled!"
we must nev - er vain - ly test."
God a - lone will I o - bey."
be the Word we hear, o - bey.

37 Firstborn of Mary

FIRSTBORN OF MARY 11 10. 11 10

First-born of Ma - ry, pro - voc - a - tive preach - er, i -

tin - er - ant teach - er, out - sid - er's choice;

Je - sus in - spires and dis - arms and con - fus - es who -

ev - er he choos - es to hear his voice.

Text: John L. Bell
Music: John L. Bell
Text and Music copyright © 1998 WGRG The Iona Community (Scotland).
Used by permission of GIA Publications, Inc., exclusive agent.

When Jesus worked here on earth 38

JESUS ON EARTH CM with refrain

1 When Je - sus worked___ here on earth he
2 The el - ders of the syn - a - gogue were
3 The way he lived was proof of it: he
4 So pass it on to - day, good friend; the

preached in his home - town, I - sa - iah's hopes___
shocked by Mar - y's son, that he was des - tined to
qui - et - ed our strife. The cross it - self___ he
mes - sage is the same. De - liv - 'rance Christ___ a -

now ful - filled, those claims of great re - nown.
be the Christ, the Christ for ev - 'ry - one.
would not flee e'en though it cost his life.
lone can give, for this to earth he came.

Refrain

To bring good news to the need - y, to make the blind to

see, the bro - ken hearts healed a - gain, to

| 1–3 | 4 |
| Am | Gm |

set the cap - tive free. set the cap - tive free.

Text: Howard S. Olson
Music: Almaz Belihu; Yemissrach Dimts Literature Program, Ethiopia
Text and Music copyright © 1993 Howard S. Olson

39 Will you come and follow me

KELVINGROVE 76. 76. 77. 76

Optional verses:

Will you leave yourself behind if I but call your name?
Will you care for cruel and kind and never be the same?
Will you risk the hostile stare
   should your life attract or scare?
Will you let me answer prayer in you and you in me?

Will you let the blinded see if I but call your name?
Will you set the prisoners free and never be the same?
Will you kiss the leper clean,
   and do such as this unseen,
and admit to what I mean in you and you in me?

Text: John L. Bell and Graham Maule
Music: Scottish traditional; arranged by John L. Bell
   Text and Music copyright © 1987, Arrangement copyright © 1995 WGRG The Iona Community (Scotland).
   Used by permission of GIA Publications, Inc., exclusive agent.

Som'landela (We will follow) 40

SOM'LANDEL' UJESU 10 9. 10 10

Zulu: Som' - lan - de - la, som' - lan - del' u - Je - su.
English: We will fol - low, we will fol - low Je - sus.

Som' - lan - de - la yo - nke in - da - wo.
We will fol - low, ev - 'ry - where he goes.

Som' - lan - de - la, som' - lan - del' u - Je - su.
We will fol - low, we will fol - low Je - sus.

La - pho E - ya - kho - na som' - lan - de - la.
Ev - 'ry - where he goes___ we will fol - low.

*Pronunciation: Sohm-lahn-deh-lah, sohm-lahn-dehl oo-Jeh-soo. Sohm-lahn-deh-lah, yohn-keh een-dah-woh.
Sohm-lahn-deh-lah, sohm-lahn-dehl oo-Jeh-soo. Lah-poh Eh-yah-koh-nah sohm-lahn-deh-lah.

Text: Zimbabwean traditional
Music: Zimbabwean traditional

41

Blessed are they

GREIF 10 7. 10 6 with refrain

	Dm			Bb			Dm		Bb	
1	Bless - ed	are	they	who	are	poor	in	spir - it,
2	Bless - ed	are	they	who	are	meek	and hum-ble,
3	Bless - ed	are	they	who	will	mourn	in	sor - row,
4	Bless those	who	hun - ger	and	thirst	for	jus - tice,
5	Bless - ed	are	they	who	show	oth - ers mer - cy,
6	Bless - ed	are	hearts	that	are	clean	and ho - ly,
7	Bless - ed	are	they	who	bring	peace	a - mong us,
8	Bless those	who	suf - fer	from	per - se - cu - tion,

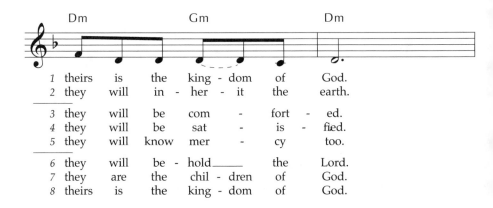

Dm Gm Dm

1 theirs is the king - dom of God.
2 they will in - her - it the earth.

3 they will be com - fort - ed.
4 they will be sat - is - fied.
5 they will know mer - cy too.

6 they will be - hold____ the Lord.
7 they are the chil - dren of God.
8 theirs is the king - dom of God.

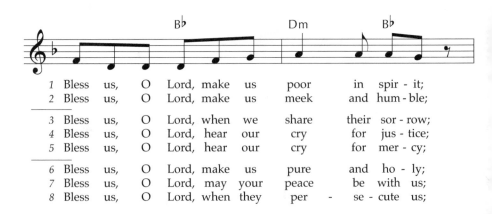

Bb Dm Bb

1 Bless us, O Lord, make us poor in spir - it;
2 Bless us, O Lord, make us meek and hum - ble;

3 Bless us, O Lord, when we share their sor - row;
4 Bless us, O Lord, hear our cry for jus - tice;
5 Bless us, O Lord, hear our cry for mer - cy;

6 Bless us, O Lord, make us pure and ho - ly;
7 Bless us, O Lord, may your peace be with us;
8 Bless us, O Lord, when they per - se - cute us;

Text: The Beatitudes; adapted by Jean Anthony Greif, alt.
Music: Jean Anthony Greif; accompaniment by Randall DeBruyn
      Text and Music copyright © 1966, 1983 Vernacular Hymns Publishing Co.

bless us, O Lord, our God.

Refrain

We are the light of the world, may our light shine be - fore all; that they may see the good that we do, and give glo - ry to God.

42 Our father, which art in heaven

MALOTTE Irregular

Our fa - ther, which art in heav - en,

hal - low - ed be thy name.

Thy king - dom come, thy will be done in

earth as it is in heav - en.

Give us this day our dai - ly bread; and for - give us our

Text: Albert H. Malotte, based on Matthew 6:9–13
Music: Albert H. Malotte

43 Lè ou pote yon kado (Remember this)

HAITIAN OFFERTORY HYMN 77. 8 10 with refrain

Text: Adonaï Jean-Juste, *Chante Iwanj Granmèt la*; translated by Julia Smucker
    Translation copyright © Julia Smucker
Music: Adonaï Jean-Juste, *Chante Iwanj Granmèt la*; arranged by Julia Smucker
    Arrangement copyright © Julia Smucker

lè	ou konn pa - ta - je,	se
lè	ou pa nan pran poz,	se
lè	ou pa me - pri - ze yo,	se
lè'w	re - kon - sil - ye a - vèk yo,	se
you	*rec - on - cile with God,*	*when*
you	*work with com - mon cause,*	*when*
you	*stand a - gainst op - pres - sion,*	*when*
you	*make peace with your broth - ers,*	*when*

lè	ou pa nan kan - ta - mwa,	se
lè	ou byen viv ak frè'w yo,	se
lè'w	kan - pe a - vèk yo tout,	se
lè	ou me - te a - vèk yo,	se
you	*share with one an - oth - er,*	*then*
you	*have peace with your broth - ers,*	*then*
you	*stand with all the low - ly,*	*then*
you	*come to - geth - er with them,*	*then*

lè	sa	Bon - dye ap pran ka - do'w yo.
lè	sa	w'ap vin po - te ka - do'w yo.
lè	sa	ka - do'w y'ap gen va - lè vre.
lè	sa	w'ap gen plas pou ka - do'w yo.
on - ly		*will your gift be ac - cept - ed.*
on - ly		*may you come to the al - tar.*
on - ly		*will God find your gift wor - thy.*
on - ly		*can your gift be ac - cept - ed.*

Percussion pattern

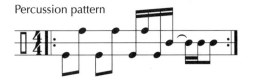

44 When Jesus the healer

HEALER 11 6 11 5

1 When Je - sus the heal - er passed through Gal - i - lee,
2 A par - a - lyzed man was let down through a roof.
3 The death of his daugh-ter caused Jai - rus to weep.
4 When blind Bar - ti - mae - us cried out to the Lord,

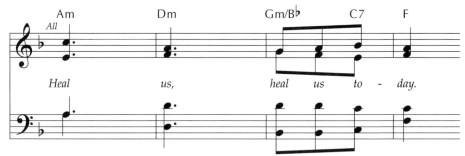

Heal us, heal us to - day.

the deaf came to hear and the blind came to see.
His sins were for - giv - en, his walk - ing the proof.
The Lord took her hand, and he raised her from sleep.
his faith made him whole and his sight was re - stored.

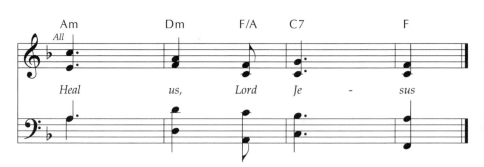

Heal us, Lord Je - sus

5 The twelve were commissioned and sent out in twos, ...
   to make the sick whole and to spread the good news. ...

6 The lepers were healed and the demons cast out. ...
   A bent woman straightened to laugh and to shout. ...

7 There's still so much sickness and suffering today. ...
   We gather together for healing, and pray, ...

Text: Peter David Smith
Music: Peter David Smith

Calm me, Lord

45

CALM ME, LORD 87. 97

Calm me, Lord, as you calmed the storm;

still me, Lord, keep me from harm.

Let all the tu - mult with - in me cease; en -

To repeat ad lib.

fold me, Lord, in your peace.

Final

Lord, en - fold me in your peace.

Text: David Adam
Copyright © SPCK, Holy Trinity Church, Marylebone Road, London NW1 4DU.
Music: Margaret Rizza
Copyright © 1998 Kevin Mayhew Ltd. Administered and sub-published in North America by GIA Publications, Inc.

46 Vin pran (Come, take and eat)

VIN PRAN 66. 66 with refrain

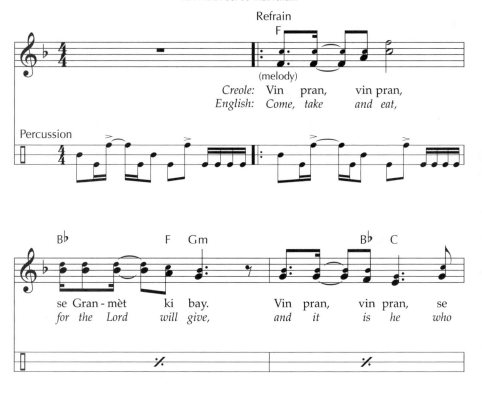

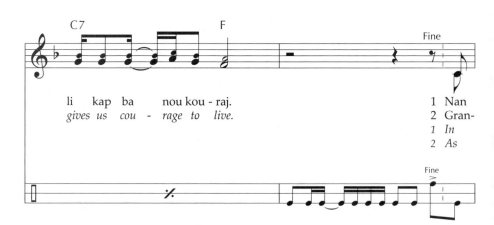

Text: Roland Lussier, O.M.I., based on Mark 8:1–10; translated by Julia Smucker
Music: Roland Lussier, O.M.I.; arranged by Julia Smucker
Translation and Arrangement copyright © Julia Smucker

sa - vann Ga - li - le, Je - zi tap pre - che moun. Nan
mèt la byen konn - en foul la kap kou - te li. You
Ga - li - lee, the Lord was preach-ing to the crowd. No-
Je - sus preached, he knew they'd come from far a - way to

kou - te y'ap kou - te, yo bli - ye yo gran - gou.
tout so - ti byen lwen pou tan - de sa l'ap di.
bod - y could af - ford to feed all those a - round.
see what he would do, to hear what he would say.

CREOLE

3 Pat genyen pase sa: de pwason ak sèt pen.
  Kat mil moun ki te la; yo tout manje vant plen.

4 Sa'k pi rèd, zanmi'm yo, lè tout moun fin manje,
  you ramase rès yo, valè sèt gwo panye.

5 Men tou sa se twòkèt, se dèyè ki gen chay.
  Pou moun ki moun pa'l nèt, se yon lòt pen l'ap bay.

6 Se kò li l'ap ba nou, pou moun ki manje li
  pa janm santi grangou, ni pou yo pa mouri.

ENGLISH

3 Some fish they had to share, and seven loaves of bread;
  four thousand people there, all went away well fed.

4 When all had had their fill, they gathered up the rest,
  and seven baskets full, no less, did they have left.

5 Now take what Jesus gives, receive him and be fed.
  To those who will be his, he'll give another bread.

6 He is the bread of life for those who eat of him.
  Not hunger, death or strife holds power over them.

47 Let the children come to me

LET THE CHILDREN COME Irregular with refrain

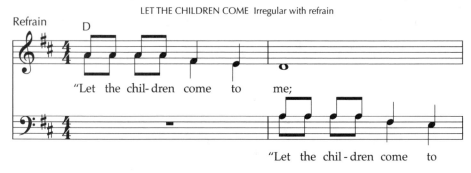

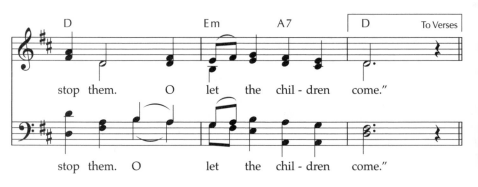

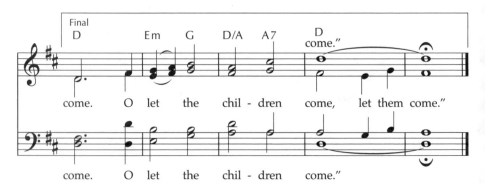

Verses

1 Peo - ple were bring - ing chil - dren
2 "If____ you seek the king - dom,
3 Then____ the Lord em - braced them,

just____ to see the Lord, and
lis - ten to what I say: Un -
held____ them in his care. With

when the dis - ci - ples stopped them,
less you be - come like chil - dren, you
love he be - stowed his bless - ing; with

this is what they heard:
can - not know the way."
love he spoke this prayer:

To Refrain

48 Come unto me

COME UNTO ME Irregular with refrain

1 Come un-to me, all ye that la - bor, and

la - bor, and I will give you rest. Come un - to

I will give you rest. Come un - to me,

me, ye that are heav-y la - den, and I will give you

ye that are heav-y la - den, and I will give you rest.

Refrain

1 rest. ...up - on thee and learn of me, for I am meek and
2 light.

Take my yoke up-on thee and learn of me, for I am meek and

Text: Bernice Johnson Reagon, based on Matthew 11:28-30
Music: Bernice Johnson Reagon

49 I will come to you in the silence

YOU ARE MINE* Irregular with refrain

1 I will come to you in the si - lence,
2 I am hope for all who are hope - less.
3 I am strength for all the de - spair - ing,
4 am the Word that leads all to free - dom, I

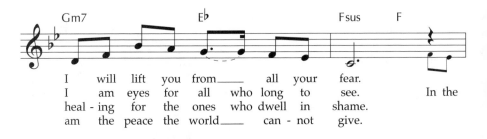

I will lift you from____ all your fear.
I am eyes for all who long to see. In the
heal - ing for the ones who dwell in shame.
am the peace the world____ can - not give.

You will hear my voice, I claim you as my choice, be
shad - ows of the night____ I will be your light,____
All the blind will see, the lame will all run free, and
I will call your name, em - brac - ing all your pain, stand

still and know I am here. *(To verse 2)*
come and rest in me. *(To refrain)*
all will know my name. *(To refrain)*
up, now walk, and live! *(To refrain)*

*Original title

Text: David Haas
Music: David Haas
    Text and Music copyright © 1991 GIA Publications, Inc.

50 Woza nomthwalo wakho (Come, bring your burdens to God)

WOZA NOMTHWALO WAKHO 77. 78

Pronunciation: Woh-zah nohm twah-loh wah-koh (3x), oo Jeh-zwah-kah soh zah tee hay.

Text: Collected by Mairi Munro from the singing of the Mooiplaas congregation, South Africa
Music: Collected by Mairi Munro from the singing of the Mooiplaas congregation, South Africa
Text and music copyright © admin. WGRG The Iona Community (Scotland)

Quién dicen que soy yo?
(Who do you say that I am?)

51

QUIÉN DICEN QUE SOY YO Irregular with refrain

Ostinato Refrain

SPANISH

1 "Dicen algunos que eres Juan Bautista.
   Otros han dicho que eres Elías."

2 "Unos han oído a otra gente que están seguros
   que eres un profeta muy antiguo que ha vuelto a la vida."

3 "¡Eres el Mesías! ¡Eres el Mesías!"

4 "Al morir por causa mía ganarán la vida eterna."

ENGLISH

1 "Some say that you are John the Baptizer.
   Others say they know that you are Elijah."

2 "Others have been hearing some who swear that they surely know
   that you are a prophet from of old and you've come back to life."

3 "You are the Messiah! You are the Messiah!"

4 "Anyone who dies for my sake will have found eternal life."

52 Whatsoever you do

WHATSOEVER YOU DO 10 10 11 with refrain

Capo 1: D / G/D / D / A
Eb / Ab/Eb / Eb / Bb

Refrain

What-so-ev-er you do to the least of my

Bm / D/A / A7 / D/A / A / D
Cm / Eb/Bb / Bb7 / Eb/Bb / Bb / Eb

peo-ple, that you do un-to me.

D / G / A / D
Eb / Ab / Bb / Eb

1 When I was hun-gry, you gave me to eat;
2 When I was home-less, you o-pened your door;
3 When I was wea-ry, you helped me find rest;
4 When I was lit-tle, you taught me to read;

G / A7 / D
Ab / Bb7 / Eb

when I was thirst-y, you gave me to drink.
when I was na-ked, you gave me your coat.
when I was anx-ious, you calmed all my fears.
when I was lone-ly, you gave me your love.

Text: Willard F. Jabusch, based on Matthew 25:31–46
Music: Willard F. Jabusch; harmonized by Robert J. Batastini
Text and Music copyright © 1966, 1982 Willard F. Jabusch; admin. OCP

Now en - ter in - to the home of my Fa - ther.

5 When in a prison, you came to my cell;
   when on a sickbed, you cared for my needs. Now enter …

6 In a strange country, you made me at home;
   seeking employment, you found me a job. Now enter …

7 Hurt in a battle, you bound up my wounds;
   searching for kindness, you held out your hand. Now enter …

8 When I was Black, or Latino, or white;
   mocked and insulted, you carried my cross. Now enter …

9 When I was aged, you bothered to smile;
   when I was restless, you listened and cared. Now enter …

10 You saw me covered with spittle and blood;
   you knew my features, though grimy with sweat. Now enter …

11 When I was lauged at, you stood by my side;
   when I was happy, you shared in my joy. Now enter …

53 Here to the house of God we come

KHAO I DANG*

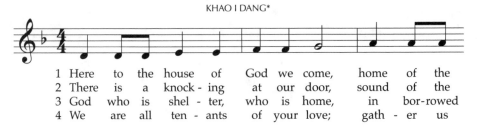

1 Here to the house of God we come, home of the
2 There is a knock-ing at our door, sound of the
3 God who is shel-ter, who is home, in bor-rowed
4 We are all ten-ants of your love; gath-er us

peo-ple of the Way, here to give thanks for
home-less of the world, voice of the fright-ened
rooms you came to live, plead-ed to save the
round a com-mon fire, warm us in com-pa -

all we have, nam-ing our needs for ev-ery day,
ref-u-gee, cry of the chil-dren in the cold,
dis-pos-sessed, cru-ci-fied, lay in bor-rowed grave:
ny with Christ, give us the heart to feel, to share

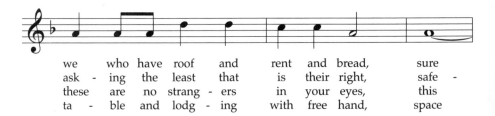

we who have roof and rent and bread, sure
ask-ing the least that is their right, safe -
these are no strang-ers in your eyes, this
ta-ble and lodg-ing with free hand, space

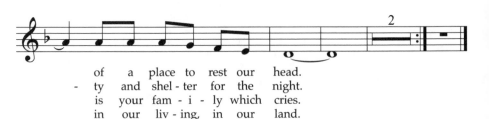

of a place to rest our head.
-ty and shel-ter for the night.
is your fam-i-ly which cries.
in our liv-ing, in our land.

*This is the name of a Cambodian refugee camp.

Text: Shirley Erena Murray
Music: Colin Alexander Gibson
Text and Music copyright © 1992 Hope Publishing Company, Carol Stream, IL 60188.
All rights reserved. Used by permission.

What does the Lord require of you? 54

MOON Irregular

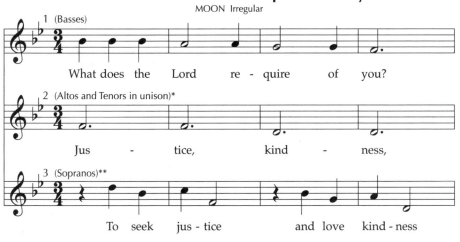

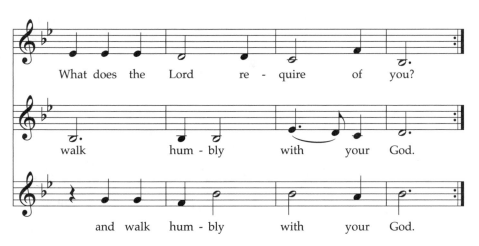

*Enter on first repeat.

**Enter on second repeat

Text: Jim Strathdee, based on Micah 6:8
Music: Jim Strathdee

55 Love the Lord your God

Irregular with refrain

With all your heart and soul

Love the Lord your God with all your heart and soul, with all your

with all your mind and strength, love the

mind and strength. Let all that is with-in you praise the

Lord your God with all your heart and soul, with all your

Lord! With all your heart and soul

mind and strength. Let all that is with-in you praise the

with all your mind and strength, praise the

Text: Patricia J. Shelly
Music: Patricia J. Shelly
Text and Music copyright © 1996 Patricia J. Shelly

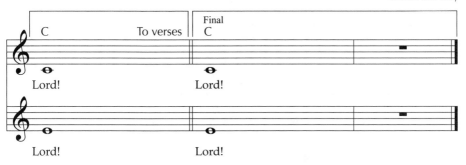

To verses | Final

Lord! Lord!

Lord! Lord!

Verses

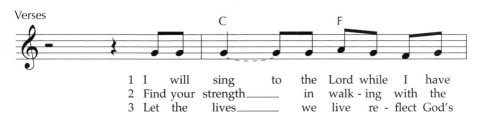

1 I will sing to the Lord while I have
2 Find your strength___ in walk - ing with the
3 Let the lives___ we live re - flect God's

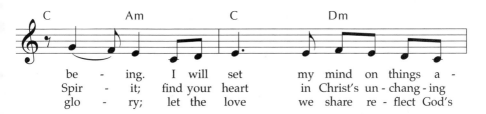

be - ing. I will set my mind on things a -
Spir - it; find your heart in Christ's un - chang - ing
glo - ry; let the love we share re - flect God's

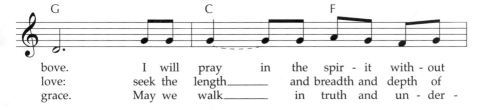

bove. I will pray in the spir - it with - out
love: seek the length___ and breadth and depth of
grace. May we walk___ in truth and un - der -

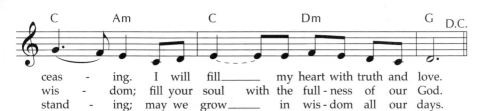

ceas - ing. I will fill___ my heart with truth and love.
wis - dom; fill your soul with the full - ness of our God.
stand - ing; may we grow___ in wis - dom all our days.

56 Unless a grain of wheat

NEVER THE BLADE SHALL RISE* Irregular with refrain

1 Un-less a grain of wheat falls to the earth,

2 The one who loves the world-ly life

3 If an-y-one would serve me,

falls to the earth and dies, it re-mains on-ly a

los-es the life so lived, while the one who hates the

come and fol-low me; come and fol-low me;

grain of wheat and nev-er the blade shall rise.

life in this world pre-serves it to life e-ter-nal.

where I am, there will my ser-vant be.

*Original title

Text: Kathy Powell, based on John 12
Music: Kathy Powell
Text and Music copyright © 1994 GIA Publications, Inc.

57 Go, my friends, in grace

BENEDICTUS DEUS 56. 66

1 Go, my friends, in grace, be - neath the
2 Walk, my friends, in peace, with - in this
3 Serve, my friends, in love, your neigh - bors
4 Come a - gain, my friends, to wor - ship

bless - ed sky. Where you go, God is
fall - en world. Where you walk, God is
and your foes. Where you serve, God is
and to pray. When we meet, God is

1–3

there, be - neath the bless - ed sky.
there, with - in this fall - en world.
there, in neigh - bors and in foes.

4

here. Ben-e-dic - tus De - us.*

*Translation: Blessed be God

Text: David Wright, 2004, *A Field of Voices*, 2007
Copyright © 2004 David Wright
Music: James E. Clemens, 2004, *A Field of Voices*, 2007
Copyright © 2004 James E. Clemens

O God, how we have wandered 58

HERZLICH TUT MICH VERLANGEN 76. 76D

1 O God, how we have wan - dered and hid - den from your face;
2 And now at length dis - cern - ing the e - vil that we do,
3 O God of all the liv - ing, both ban-ished and re - stored,

in fool-ish-ness have squan-dered your leg - a - cy of grace.
by faith we are re - turn - ing with hope and trust in you.
com - pas-sion-ate, for - giv - ing, our peace and hope as - sured.

But how, in ex - ile dwell - ing, we turn with fear and shame,
In haste you come to meet us, and home re - joic-ing bring,
Grant now that our trans - gress - ing, our faith-less-ness may cease.

as dis - tant but com-pell - ing, you call us each by name.
in glad-ness there to greet us with calf and robe and ring.
Stretch out your hand in bless - ing, in par - don, and in peace.

Text: Msgr. Kevin Nichols, *Resource Collection of Hymns and Service Music for the Liturgy*, alt.
Copyright © 1981 International Committee on English in the Liturgy, Inc. All rights reserved.
Music: Hans Leo Hassler, *Lustgarten neuer Deutscher Gesäng*, 1601; harmonized by J. S. Bach, *St. Matthew Passion*, 1729

59 From ashes to the living fount

ST. FLAVIAN CM

1 From ash - es to the liv - ing fount your
2 Through fast - ing, prayer, and char - i - ty your
3 *(below)*
4 From ash - es to the liv - ing fount, your

church must jour - ney, Lord, bap - tized in grace, in
voice speaks deep with - in, re - turn - ing us to
church must jour - ney still, through cross and tomb to

grace re - newed by your most ho - ly word.
ways of truth and turn - ing us from sin.

Eas - ter joy, in Spir - it - fire ful - filled.

SUNDAYS I & II

3 From desert to the mountaintop
   in Christ our way we see,
   so, tempered by temptation's might
   we might transfigured be.

SUNDAY III

3 For thirsting hearts let waters flow,
   our fainting souls revive;
   and at the well your waters give
   our everlasting life.

SUNDAY IV

3 We sit beside the road and plead,
   "Come, save us, David's son!"
   Now with your vision heal our eyes,
   the world's true Light alone.

SUNDAY V

3 Our graves split open, bring us back,
   your promise to proclaim;
   to darkened tombs call out, "Arise!"
   and glorify your name.

Text: Alan J. Hommerding
    Copyright © 1994 World Library Publications, 3708 River Road, Suite 400, Franklin Park, IL 60131-2158. www.wlpmusic.com
    All rights reserved. Used by permission.
Music: *John's Day Psalter*, 1562; harmonization based on the original *faux-bourdon* setting

Come to me, come to us

60

COME TO US* 11 9. 10 10

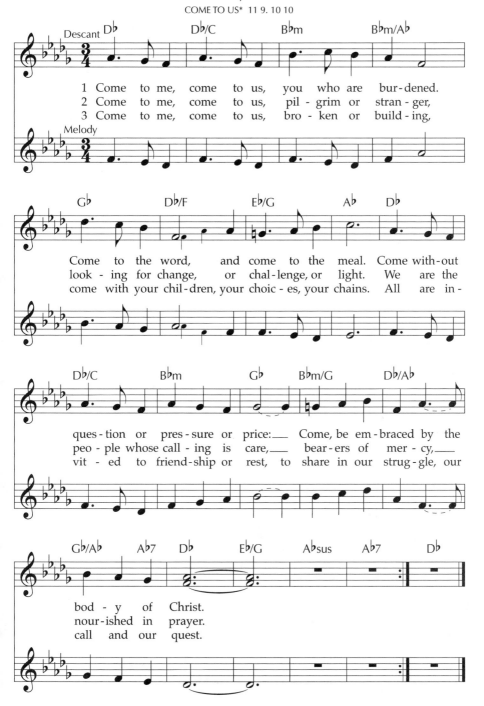

1 Come to me, come to us, you who are bur-dened.
2 Come to me, come to us, pil-grim or stran-ger,
3 Come to me, come to us, bro-ken or build-ing,

Come to the word, and come to the meal. Come with-out
look - ing for change, or chal-lenge, or light. We are the
come with your chil-dren, your choic - es, your chains. All are in -

ques - tion or pres - sure or price:___ Come, be em-braced by the
peo - ple whose call - ing is care,___ bear-ers of mer - cy,___
vit - ed to friend-ship or rest, to share in our strug-gle, our

bod - y of Christ.
nour-ished in prayer.
call and our quest.

*Original title

Text: Rory Cooney
Music: Rory Cooney
Text and Music copyright © 1986 North American Liturgy Resources. Published by OCP.

61 O God, to whom then shall I turn?

FRUYTIERS 89. 89. 88 10

1 O God, to whom then shall I turn? Come, now pro-
2 Wan-d'ring a - lone through E - gypt's land, dai - ly I
3 But I re - turned to God, my Lord, once and for
4 Then at the end of life's short span, Christ, our sal -

tect me as I wan - der. I am sur - round-ed day and
sinned, your name re - nounc - ing. There I was seen a wor - thy
all the world for - sak - ing. Rich - es of E - gypt fad - ed
va - tion, there a - waits us. "Come, child," says God, "re - ceive your

night by foes that seek my soul to slan - der. O God, your
guest, un - trou - bled by the world a - round me. Trapped, with-out
soon as Christ his peace e - ter - nal gave me. They who de -
crown; here dwell for - ev - er with the an - gels." Tears shall be

Text: Menno Simons, 16th c.; adapted by Kenneth Nafziger, 1996
Music: Jan Fruytiers Ecclesiasticus, 1565; harmonized by Jan van Biezen

spir - it grant to me so I in life might faith - ful
hope, in e - vil's noose, not fear - ing I my life might
sire to en - ter life, though in a world where sin is
wiped from ev - 'ry eye. No one will suf - fer pain or

be, and in your pres - ence dwell e - ter - nal - ly.
lose, I gave my - self un - to the dev - il's cause.
rife, must stay the course through tri - als, tests and strife.
die. Let us Christ Je - sus' name now glo - ri - fy!

62 Create in me a clean heart

CLEAN HEART Irregular with refrain

Cre - ate in me a clean heart, O God, and re -

new a right spir - it with - in me. Cre -

spir - it with - in me. spir - it with - in me.

And re - new a right spir - it with - in me.

Text: Andrew Kreider, based on Psalm 51
Music: Andrew Kreider
Text and Music copyright © 1994 Andrew Kreider

Verses

Bm7   *Solo or unison*   Em7

1 Have mer - cy   on   me,   O   God,
2 I   know   that   I____   have sinned.
3 You   look   for   truth with - in   me.
4 Re - store   to   me____   your   joy.

Cmaj7   Bm7   B♭m7

ac - cord - ing   to   your stead - fast   love._____
for   my   trans - gres - sions are   be - fore   me._____
Teach me   your   wis - dom   in   my   heart._____
Sus - tain   in   me   a   will - ing   spir - it._____

Am7   *All, in harmony*   Cmaj7   G

Come wash me   clean from my   in - iq - ui - ty,   and

F   Am7   C   D   E♭

D.S.

cleanse me from my   sin,   O   Lord.   Cre-

63

Herr, füll mich neu
(God, fill me now)

48. 48 with refrain

German:

1 Herr, füll mich neu, füll mich neu mit dei-nem Geis-te,
2 Herr, füll mich neu, füll mich neu mit dei-ner Lie-be,
3 Herr, füll mich neu, füll mich neu mit dei-nem Glau-ben,
4 Herr, füll mich neu, füll mich neu mit dei-ner Freu-de,

English:

1 God, fill me now, fill me with your Ho-ly Spir-it.
2 God, fill me now, fill me with your lov-ing kind-ness.
3 God, fill me now, with a con-stant faith a-bid-ing.
4 God, fill me now, fill me now with joy and glad-ness,

1 der mich be-lebt und zu dir, mein Gott, hin-zie-het!
2 die bei dir bleibt und mit Freu-den Las-ten trä-get!
3 der auf dich schaut und in an-dern Glau-ben we-cket!
4 die ü-ber-strömt und in Lob und Preis dich rüh-met!

1 You give me life, and you draw me to your pres-ence.
2 Those who stay close will with joy their bur-dens car-ry.
3 Look-ing to you will a-wak-en faith in oth-ers.
4 so that my heart o-ver-flows with joy-ous prais-es!

Text: Kommunität Gnadenthal; tr. Jean Janzen, Kenneth Nafziger, and Randall Spaulding, 2006
Music: Klaus Heizmann, 2004
Text and Music copyright © Präsenz, Kunst, & Buch, Gnadenthal, 65597 Hünfelden, Germany
Translation copyright © 2006 Jean Janzen, Kenneth Nafziger, and Randall Spaulding

Refrain

Hier bin ich vor dir. Leer sind mei - ne
Here be - fore you now; see, my hands are

Hän - de. Herr, füll mich ganz mit dir!
emp - ty. God, fill me now with you.

64 There is a well (Un pozo hay)

THERE IS A WELL Irregular

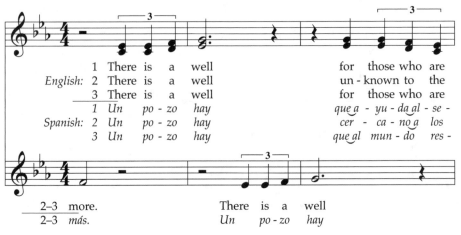

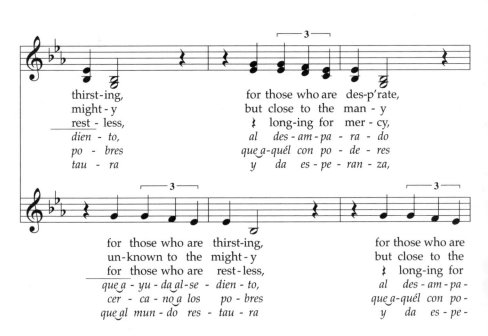

Text: Tom Conry; Spanish tr. by Jaime Cortez
Music: Tom Conry
Text and Music copyright © 1993 TEAM Publications. Published by OCP.

the bro-ken and poor.
with noth-ing in store.
cre - a - tion re - stored.
que su - fre do - lor.
no pue - de ha - llar.
jus - ti - cia y paz.

Where those who

des - p'rate, the bro-ken and poor.
man - y with noth-ing in store.
mer - cy, cre - a - tion re - stored.
ra - do que su - fre do - lor.
de - res no pue - de ha - llar.
ran - za, jus - ti - cia y paz.

drink from the wa-ters be - neath them;
mar de las a - guas que bro - tan,

Those who drink from the wa-ters be -
Y al to - mar de las a - guas que

they shall live al - ways and thirst no
vi - da se en - cuen - tra, sed, nun - ca

neath them; they shall live al - ways
bro - tan, vi - da se en - cuen - tra,

1, 2

more.
más.

3

more.
más.

and thirst no
sed, nun - ca

and thirst no more.
sed, nun - ca más.

65 Abre mis ojos (Open my eyes)

ABRE MIS OJOS Irregular

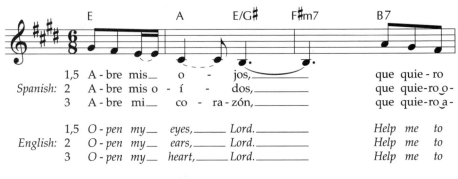

1,5 A - bre mis__ o - jos,_____ que quie - ro
Spanish: 2 A - bre mis o - í - dos,_____ que quie-ro_o-
3 A - bre mi__ co - ra-zón,_____ que quie-ro_a-

1,5 O - pen my__ eyes,_____ Lord._____ Help me to
English: 2 O - pen my__ ears,_____ Lord._____ Help me to
3 O - pen my__ heart,_____Lord._____ Help me to

ver co - mo tú. A - bre mis__ o - jos,_____
ír co - mo tú. A - bre mis o - í - dos,_____
mar co - mo tú. A - bre mi__ co - ra-zón,_____

see your____ face. O - pen my__ eyes,_____ Lord._____
hear your____ voice. O - pen my__ ears,_____ Lord._____
love like____ you. O - pen my__ heart,_____ Lord._____

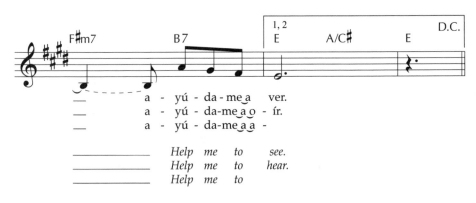

__ a - yú - da-me_a ver.
__ a - yú - da-me_a_o - ír.
__ a - yú - da-me_a_a -

_____ Help me to see.
_____ Help me to hear.
_____ Help me to

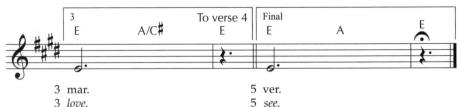

3 mar. 5 ver.
3 love. 5 see.

Text: Jesse Manibusan, based on Mark 8:22–25 and Psalm 51:12–14; Rufino Zaragoza, OFM, Spanish verses 1–3 and 5
Copyright © 1988, 1998, 2001 Jesse Manibusan and Rufino Zaragoza, OFM. Published by OCP. All rights reserved.
Verse 4 in Spanish copyright © 1982 SOBICAIN. All rights reserved.
Music: Jesse Manibusan
Copyright © 1988, 1998, 1999 Jesse Manibusan. Published by OCP. All rights reserved.

Verse 4

4 Da - me la a - le - grí - a___ de tu
4 And the first___ shall be last,___ and our

sal - va - ción,___ cre-a en mí un co-ra-zón__ pu -
eyes are o - pened and we'll hear___ like__ nev-er be -

ro.___ No me a - rro - jes___ le - jos de tu ros-tro, Se -
fore.___ And we'll speak in new ways,___ and we'll see God's__

ñor, no me qui - tes tu san - to es - pí - ri - tu.___
face in__ plac - es___ we've nev-er known.___

66 While I keep silence

SILENCE 86. 86. 86

1 While I keep si - lence, si - lence,
2 My thirst - ing spir - it, spir - it,
3 All you who wan - der, wan - der,

si - lence in my flesh, my mer - est bod - y
spir - it wastes a - way; I with - er in the
wan - der with - out hope, who know your man - y

fails. My sins grow bit - ter, bit - ter,
sun. But as I'm turn - ing, turn - ing,
sins, seek out the Sav - ior, Sav - ior,

bit - ter in my mouth. My bones re - turn to
turn - ing toward the night, you split the si - lent
Sav - ior while he's found; he hides you in his

dust. O God, I groan both day and
skies. O God, I stand be - neath the
hand. O God, you hear us day and

night, be - neath your heav - y hand.
rain, be - neath the cleans - ing rain.
night; re - store us by your hand.

*These notes may be hummed throughout the hymn, beginning at these places.

Text: David Wright, based on Psalm 32:3-5, 2005, *A Field of Voices*, 2007
   Copyright © 2005 David Wright
Music: James E. Clemens, 2005, *A Field of Voices*, 2007
   Copyright © 2005 James E. Clemens

Khudaya, rahem kar (Have mercy on us, Lord)

67

KHUDAYA, RAHEM KAR 65. 65. 65

Unison, unaccompanied

Urdu: 1,3 Khu - da - ya, ra - hem kar. Khu - da - ya ra-
English: 1,3 Have mer - cy on us, Lord, have mer - cy on

hem, khu - da - ya, ra - hem kar. Khu - da - ya ra-
us. Have mer - cy on us, Lord, have mer - cy on

hem. Khu - da - ya ra - hem kar, khu - da - ya ra - hem.
us. Have mer - cy on us, Lord, have mer - cy on us.

2 Ma - si - ha, ra - hem kar, ma - si - ha, ra-
2 Have mer - cy on us, Christ, have mer - cy on

hem. Ma - si - ha ra - hem kar, ma - si - ha, ra-
us. Have mer - cy on us, Christ have mer - cy on

hem. Ma - si - ha, ra - hem kar, ma - si - ha, ra - hem.
us. Have mer - cy on us, Christ have mer - cy on us.

The symbol ○ indicates when finger cymbals may be played.

Text: traditional liturgical, Pakistan
Music: R. F. Liberius, Pakistan

68

Kyrie

KYRIE (REINDORF) 77. 77

Translation: Lord, have mercy.

Voices can enter in this order: alto, bass, soprano, tenor 1, tenor 2.

Text: Greek litany
Music: Dinah Reindorf; parts as taught by Ysaye Maria Barnwell, Laurelville 2007
    Tune copyright © 1987 Dinah Reindorf

Ya hamalaLah (O Lamb of God) 69

YA HAMALALAH Irregular

Text: Yusuf Khill, Palestine/Israel
Music: Yusuf Khill, Palestine/Israel

70

For God alone

FOR GOD ALONE

English: For God a - lone my soul a - waits in
German: Auf Gott al - lein harrt mei - ne See - le,
French: C'est Dieu seul que mon âme at - tend en
Spanish: Mi al - ma es - pe - ra so - lo a Dios en

si - lence.
stil - le.
si - len - ce.
si - len - cio.

Text: Eleanor Daley; German translation by Dorothea Wulfhorst; French translation by Marc Chambron;
  Spanish translation by Martin Junge
Music: Eleanor Daley
  Text and Music copyright © 2003 Oxford University Press

Gentle God, when we are driven 71

TAWA 87. 87. 77

1 Gen - tle God, when we are driv - en past the
2 Gen - tle Spir - it, when our rea - son clouds in
3 In the mir - ror of earth's mad - ness let us
4 Let our strength be in for - giv - ing as for -

lim - its of our love, when our hurt would have a
an - ger, twists in fear, when we strike in - stead of
see our rav - aged face, in the tur - moil of all
giv - en we must be, one to one in cost - ly

weap - on and the hawk de - stroy the dove, at the
strok - ing, when we bruise and sting and smear, cool our
peo - ple let com - pas - sion find a place, touch our
lov - ing, find - ing trust and grow - ing free, gen - tle

cost of seem - ing weak, help us turn the oth - er cheek.
burn - ing, take our pain, bring us to our - selves a - gain.
hearts to make a - mends, see our en - e - mies as friends.
God, be our re - lease, gen - tle Spir - it, teach us peace.

72 We are often tossed and driv'n

BY AND BY 77. 15. 77. 11 with refrain

1 We are of-ten tossed and driv'n on the rest-less sea of time,
2 We are of-ten des-ti-tute of the things that life de-mands,
3 Tri-als dark on ev-'ry hand, and we can-not un-der-stand
4 Temp - ta-tions, hid-den snares of-ten take us un-a-wares,

som-ber skies and howl-ing tem-pest oft suc-ceed a bright sun-shine;
want of food and want of shel-ter, thirst-y hills and bar-ren lands;
all the ways that God would lead us to that bless-ed prom-ised land;
and our hearts are made to bleed for many a thought-less word or deed;

in that land of per-fect day, when the mists have rolled a-way,
we are trust-ing in the Lord, and ac-cord-ing to his word,
but he guides us with his eye, and we'll fol-low till we die;
and we won-der why the test when we try to do our best;

Text: Charles A. Tindley
Music: Charles A. Tindley; arranged by F. A. Clark

we will un-der-stand it bet-ter by and by. (by and by.)
we will un-der-stand it bet-ter by and by. (by and by.)
for we'll un-der-stand it bet-ter by and by. (by and by.)
but we'll un-der-stand it bet-ter by and by. (by and by.)

Refrain

By and by when the morn-ing comes, when the saints of

God are gath-ered home, we'll tell the sto - ry, how we've o-ver-come;

for we'll un-der-stand it bet-ter by and by. (by and by.)

73

Jesus is coming

PAVE THE WAY WITH BRANCHES*

Je - sus is com - ing. Pave the way with branch-es.

Je - sus is com - ing. Ho - san - na. san - na. Ho-

Refrain

san - na, Je - sus is com - ing. Ho -

san - na to the Prince of Peace. Ho - Prince of Peace.

Additional verses:
Release for the captives. Pave the way with branches. Release for the captives. Hosanna. *Refrain*
Hope for the down trod …
Land for the landless …
Debts are forgiven …
Feel free to create your own additional verses as needed.

*Original title

Text: Bret Hesla
Music: Bret Hesla

Hosanna! Hosanna!

74

SKO HESTEN Irregular

"Ho-san-na! Ho-san-na! Ho-san-na," we bring to Je-sus, our
san-na! Ho-san-na!" We joy-ful-ly raise our voic-es in

King, "Ho-san-na!" we sing. "Ho-
"Ho-san - na!" we sing. praise for

praise for all of our
for

days. How bless-ed is he who comes in the name of
all our days.

God, the Al-might - y One. "Ho - san-na! Ho - san-na! Ho-
God, God, the Al-might-y One.

san-na," we sing to God's own be-got-ten Son.
God's own Son.

Text: John Ylvisaker, based on Matthew 21:9
Copyright © 1991 John C. Ylvisaker
Music: Norwegian traditional; arranged by James E. Clemens, 2007
Arrangement copyright © 2007 James E. Clemens

75 Heri ni jina (Blessed be the name)

HERI NI JINA 558D 448D

He - ri ni ji - na, he - ri ni ji - na, he - ri ni ji - na la Ye-
Bless-ed be the name, bless-ed be the name, bless-ed be the name, Je-sus'

su. He - ri ni ji - na, he - ri ni ji - na,
name. Bless - ed be the name, bless - ed be the name,

he - ri ni ji - na la Ye - su. (A - mi - ni!)
bless - ed be the name, Je - sus' name. (Be - lieve!)

Al - le - lu-ya, al - le - lu-ya. He - ri ni ji - na la Ye-
Al - le - lu-ia, al - le - lu-ia. Bless - ed be the name, Je-sus'

su. (A - mi - ni!) Al - le - lu-ya, al - le - lu-ya.
name. (Be - lieve!) Al - le - lu-ia, al - le - lu-ia.

He - ri ni ji - na la Ye - su.
Bless - ed be the name, Je - sus' name.

Pronunciation: hair-ee nee jee-nah lah yeh-soo (ah-mee-nee)

Text: taught by Deogratias Mahamba
Music: east African traditional; arranged by Mark Sedio
Text and Arrangement copyright © 2003 Augsburg Fortress. Used by permission.

Prepare a room for me

76

SOUTHWELL SM

1 "Pre - pare a room for me, your
2 This room we have pre - pared; the
3 "Where e - ven two or three have
4 Lord Christ, we seek the food your
5 "My prom - ise I will keep; your
6 All thanks and praise to you, our

1 Sav - ior, Host and Priest, where I may gath - er
2 ta - ble now is set. We wait your prom - ised
3 come the meal to share, un - seen, but liv - ing,
4 grace a - lone can give. We come with emp - ty,
5 hun - ger will be fed, for in this meal I
6 Sav - ior, Lord and Friend, that through this loaf and

1 you, my friends, to cel - e - brate the feast."
2 pres - ence, Lord, where we once more are met.
3 lov - ing still, I sure - ly will be there!"
4 hun - g'ring hearts that we may eat and live.
5 of - fer you my - self, the liv - ing bread!"
6 cup you share your love that has no end!

This hymn can be sung in alternating verses by a soloist and congregation.

Text: Herman G. Stuempfle, Jr.
    Copyright © 2000 GIA Publications, Inc.
Music: W. Damon's *Psalmes of David*, 1579

77 Here is the bread

HERE IS THE BREAD 10 4 4. 10 9

1 Here is the bread that is bro - ken for you.
2 Here is the cup that I of - fer to you.
3 This is the task I am giv - ing to you:
4 Eat this and drink in re - mem - brance of me.

Take it and eat, take it and eat.
Take it and drink, take it and drink.
Be full of love, be full of love.
I am the way, I am the way.

Here is the bread that is bro - ken for you, if you
Here is the cup that I of - fer to you, come re -
This is the task I am giv - ing to you, love each
Eat this and drink in re - mem - brance of me, till we

eat, you will hun - ger no more.
ceive the for - give - ness of sins.
oth - er as I have loved you.
eat in the king - dom of God.

Text: Celah K. Pence, 2002
Music: Celah K. Pence, 2002
Text and Music copyright © 2002 Celah K. Pence

Lord Jesus, as the shadows long 78

HERZLIEBSTER JESU 11 11 11. 5

1 Lord Jesus, as the shadows long are stealing across your path, we turn and see you kneeling with towel in hand, the servant way revealing, all for our healing.

2 Strange majesty we find at work before us as we, unnerved, take up the ready chorus, "Keep back, great Lord, we rather would revere you than be so near you."

3 Yet still you come, on God's low road persisting, from force and power so quietly desisting, your every act upon love's way insisting. Quell our resisting!

Text: Leith Fisher
Copyright © Leith Fisher
Music: Johann Crüger, *Neues vollkömliches Gesangbuch, Vol. II*, 1640; harmonized by J. S. Bach

79 Holy Spirit, come to us

Text: John 13:35, 15:12–13; I John 3:16, 4:10, 16
Music: Jacques Berthier

3 Je-sus said, "No one has great-er love than this:

to lay down one's life for those one loves."

4 We know love by this, that

Christ laid down his life for us. 5 This is

love: it is not we who have loved God

but God who loved us. 6 God is love,

and those who a-bide in love a-bide in God and God in them.

*Choose either part

80 Jesus walked this lonesome valley

LONESOME VALLEY 88. 10 8

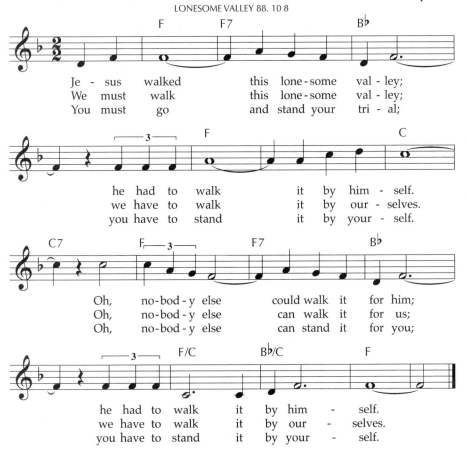

Je - sus   walked   this lone - some   val - ley;
We   must   walk   this lone - some   val - ley;
You   must   go   and stand your   tri - al;

he had to   walk   it   by him - self.
we have to   walk   it   by our - selves.
you have to   stand   it   by your - self.

Oh,   no-bod - y else   could walk it   for him;
Oh,   no-bod - y else   can walk it   for us;
Oh,   no-bod - y else   can stand it   for you;

he had to   walk   it   by him   -   self.
we have to   walk   it   by our   -   selves.
you have to   stand   it   by your   -   self.

Text: traditional spiritual
Music: traditional spiritual

When we are tempted

81

FAITH 10 10. 10 6

When we are temp - ted to de - ny your
When we are temp - ted to be - tray your
When we for - get the cross that held your
When doubt ob - scures the vic - tory of your

Son, be - cause we fear the an - ger of the
Son, be - cause he leads us in a hard - er
Son, and would a - void the bur - den of this
Son, and faith is weak and all re - solve has

world, and we are few who bear the in - sults
way, and makes de - mands we do not want to
life, the cry for jus - tice, and an end to
fled, help us to know him ris - en from the

hurled: your will, O God, be done.
pay: your will, O God, be done.
strife: your will, O God, be done.
dead: your will, O God, be done.

Text: David W. Romig
Music: J. Harold Moyer, 1965, The Mennonite Hymnal, 1969
Copyright © 1969 Faith and Life Press/Mennonite Publishing House

82

How long, O Lord

HOW LONG, O LORD 86. 886

1 How long, O Lord, will you for-get an an-swer to my
2 How long, O Lord, will you for-sake and leave me in this
3 How long, O Lord? But you for-give with mer-cy from a -

prayer?   No to-ken of   your love I see,
way?   When will you come   to my re-lief?
bove.   I find that all   your ways are just,

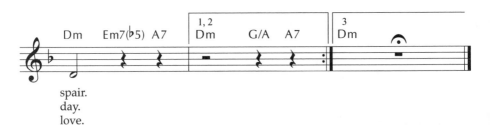

your face is turned a - way from me; I wres-tle with de -
My heart is o - ver-whelmed with grief, by e - vil night and
I learn to praise you and to trust in your un - fail - ing

spair.
day.
love.

Text: Barbara Woollett, based on Psalm 13

Music: Christopher Norton

Remember me

83

REMEMBER ME 87

1 Re - mem - ber me, re - mem - ber
2 O God, I stretch my hands to
3 If thou with - draw thy - self from

me, O Lord, re - mem - ber me.
thee, no oth - er help I know.
me, O whith - er shall I go?

Text: traditional African-American spiritual, verse 1; Charles Wesley, verses 2-3, *Psalms and Hymns*, 1741, alt.
Music: traditional African-American spiritual; harmonized by Leon C. Roberts, from *The Mass of St. Augustine*
Harmonization copyright © 1981 G.I.A. Publications, Inc.

84
So much wrong

98. 98 with refrain

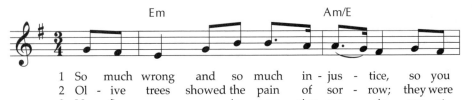

Em · · · · · · · · · · · · · Am/E

1 So much wrong and so much in - jus - tice, so you
2 Ol - ive trees showed the pain of sor - row; they were
3 No fine song, no im - pres - sive mu - sic can at -
4 Ev - 'ry - thing I could ev - er of - fer could not

Em · · · · · · Am/E · · Em

shoul - dered a wood - en cross. Now like you, my best dreams are
griev - ing___ for their Lord. Round Je - rusa - lem the hills were
tempt to re - lieve my heart; in this hour I am called to
pay for what God has done; but my life shall be spent in

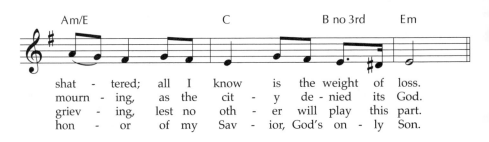

Am/E · · · · · · · C · · · B no 3rd · Em

shat - tered; all I know is the weight of loss.
mourn - ing, as the cit - y de - nied its God.
griev - ing, lest no oth - er will play this part.
hon - or of my Sav - ior, God's on - ly Son.

Refrain Em · D/F♯ · G · · · · · G/D · D · B7

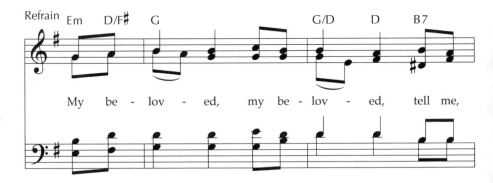

My be - lov - ed, my be - lov - ed, tell me,

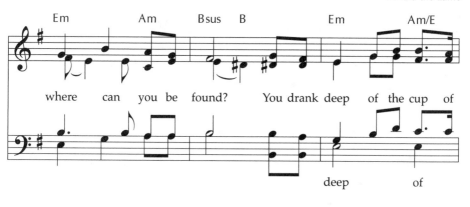

where can you be found? You drank deep of the cup of

deep of

suf - f'ring, and your death is our ho - ly ground.

85 Lay down your head

RESTING 84. 84D

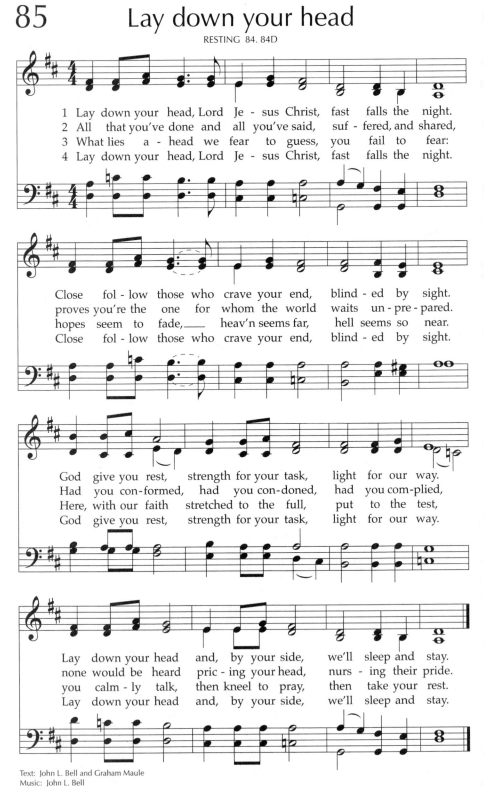

1 Lay down your head, Lord Je - sus Christ, fast falls the night.
2 All that you've done and all you've said, suf - fered, and shared,
3 What lies a - head we fear to guess, you fail to fear:
4 Lay down your head, Lord Je - sus Christ, fast falls the night.

Close fol - low those who crave your end, blind - ed by sight.
proves you're the one for whom the world waits un - pre - pared.
hopes seem to fade,___ heav'n seems far, hell seems so near.
Close fol - low those who crave your end, blind - ed by sight.

God give you rest, strength for your task, light for our way.
Had you con - formed, had you con - doned, had you com - plied,
Here, with our faith stretched to the full, put to the test,
God give you rest, strength for your task, light for our way.

Lay down your head and, by your side, we'll sleep and stay.
none would be heard pric - ing your head, nurs - ing their pride,
you calm - ly talk, then kneel to pray, then take your rest.
Lay down your head and, by your side, we'll sleep and stay.

Text: John L. Bell and Graham Maule
Music: John L. Bell

Thank you for the night

86

COMPLIMENT 5 6 10

Thank you for the night, the sign that day is
Thank you for the quiet as si - lence scat - ters
Thank you for the dark to com - pli - ment the
Thank you for the word, which dark - ness can't con -
Thank you for the night, a mea - sure of your

done, that life is meant to
sound, while God, in both, is
light, as in - sight, o - pen -
tain, that life, laid down, is
care. In dark - ness, as in

rest and sleep to come.
wait - ing to be found.
eyed, re - plac - es sight.
raised to life a - gain.
light, you, Lord, are there.

Text: John L. Bell and Graham Maule, *The Courage to Say No: Songs for Lent and Easter*, 1996
Music: John L. Bell

87

Alleluia

BYZANTINE ALLELUIA* 13 13 13

*Original title

Music: Byzantine traditional; arranged by Jeffrey Honoré
Arrangement copyright © 2005 World Library Publications, 3708 River Road, Suite 400, Franklin Park, IL 60131-2158.
www.wlpmusic.com

That Easter morn, at break of day 88

O FILII ET FILIAE 888 with alleluias

Refrain (All)

Al - le - lu - ia, al - le - lu - ia, al - le - lu - ia!

1 That Eas - ter morn, at break of day,
2 When Ma - ry's heart was filled with gloom
3 "Why do you weep?" his ques - tion came.
4 No lon - ger weep - ing, an - guish-bent,

a faith - ful wo - man went her way to seek the
and she stood weep - ing near the tomb, a stran - ger
"Whose is the bod - y you would claim?" And then, at
but with re - joic - ing Ma - ry went, by Christ as

tomb where Je - sus lay. Al - le - lu - ia!
spoke, she knew not whom. Al - le - lu - ia!
last, he spoke her name. Al - le - lu - ia!
first a - pos - tle sent. Al - le - lu - ia!

To refrain

Text: John Tisserand, d. 1494, stanza 1; translated by John Mason Neale, 1818-1866, alt. and adapted;
Delores Dufner, OSB, stanzas 2-4
Stanzas 2-4 copyright © 1994, 2003 GIA Publications, Inc.
Music: French, 15th c.; harmonized by James E. Clemens, 2006
Harmonization copyright © 2006 James E. Clemens

89

Christ is alive

CHRIST IS ALIVE 98. 98 with refrain

Refrain

Christ is a-live, and goes be-fore us to show and share what

show and

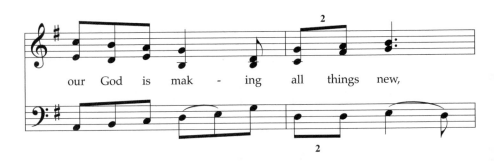

love can do. This is a day of new be-gin-nings;

share what love can do. This day new be-gin - nings;

our God is mak - ing all things new,

Fine

our God is mak - ing all things new.

Text: Brian Wren
Copyright © 1983 Hope Publishing Company, Carol Stream, IL 60188. All rights reserved. Used by permission.
Music: Lori True
Copyright © 2003 GIA Publications, Inc.

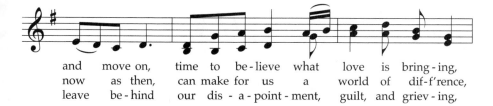

1 This is a day of new be-gin-nings, time to re-mem-ber,
2 For by the life and death of Je - sus, love's might-y Spir - it,
3 Then let us, with the Spir - it's dar - ing, step from the past, and

and move on, time to be-lieve what love is bring-ing,
now as then, can make for us a world of dif-f'rence,
leave be-hind our dis - a - point-ment, guilt, and griev-ing,

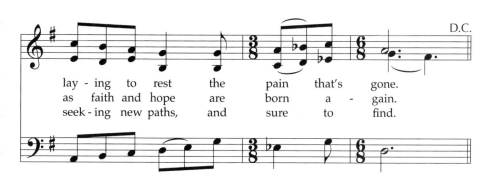

D.C.

lay - ing to rest the pain that's gone.
as faith and hope are born a - gain.
seek - ing new paths, and sure to find.

90 Oh, qué bueno es Jesús (Oh, how good is Christ the Lord)

OH, QUÉ BUENO 77. 76 with refrain

Spanish: Oh, qué bue - no es Je - sús. Que por mí mu -
English: Oh, how good is Christ the Lord! On the cross he

rió en la cruz. Mis pe - ca - dos per - do - nó.
died for me. He has par - doned all my sin.

Refrain

A su nom - bre glo - ria. A su nom - bre glo - ria.
Glo-ry be to Je - sus. Glo-ry be to Je - sus!

A su nom - bre glo - ria. En tres días re -
Glo-ry be to Je - sus! In three days he

su - ci - tó. A su nom - bre glo - ria.
rose a - gain. Glo-ry be to Je - sus!

Text: Puerto Rican traditional
Music: Puerto Rican traditional; arranged by James E. Clemens, 2001
    Arrangement copyright © 2001 James E. Clemens

Star of the morning

CHRISTE SANCTORUM 11 11 11 6

1 Star of the morn - ing, wak - ing all cre -
a - tion, sun of God's jus - tice, Je - sus, our sal -
va - tion, ris - en in splen - dor, light of ev - 'ry
na - tion: Christ, end - less dawn, be praised!

2 Font for the wea - ry, liv - ing wa - ter
flow - ing, bath - ing, re - fresh - ing, bless - ing all things
grow - ing, bring - ing to har - vest seed of gos - pel
sow - ing: Christ, spring of life, be praised!

3 Vine of God's gar - den, green - est ves - ture
wear - ing, crim - son your clus - ters, branch - es rich - ly
bear - ing, fruit for the press - ing, fin - est wine pre -
par - ing: Christ, cup of love, be praised!

4 Com - ing in glo - ry, rais - ing up the
sleep - ing, heal - ing the brok - en, com - fort - ing the
weep - ing, feast - ing your peo - ple, ev - 'ry prom - ise
keep - ing: Christ, all our joy, be praised!

Text: Delores Dufner, OSB
Copyright © 2001, 2003 GIA Publications, Inc.
Music: French church melody, *Paris Antiphoner*, 1681

92 Sing with all the saints in glory

HYMN TO JOY 87. 87D

1 Sing with all the saints in glo - ry, sing the res - ur - rec - tion song! Death and sor - row, earth's dark sto - ry, to the for - mer days be - long. All a - round the clouds are break - ing, soon the storms of

2 O what glo - ry, far ex - ceed - ing all that eye has yet per - ceived! Ho - liest hearts for a - ges plead - ing, nev - er that full joy con - ceived. God has prom - ised, Christ pre - pares it, there on high our

3 Life e - ter - nal! heav'n re - joic - es: Je - sus lives who once was dead; shout with joy, O death - less voic - es! Child of God, lift up your head! Pa - tri - archs from dis - tant a - ges, saints all long - ing

4 Life e - ter - nal! O what won - ders crowd on faith; what joy un - known, when, a - midst earth's clos - ing thun - ders, saints shall stand be - fore the throne! O to en - ter that bright por - tal, see that glow - ing

Text: William J. Irons, 1873, based on 1 Corinthians 15:20, alt.
Music: Ludwig van Beethoven, 1823; adapted by Edward Hodges, *Trinity Collection of Church Music*, 1864, alt.

time shall cease; we a - wak - en in God's like - ness,
wel - come waits; ev - 'ry hum - ble spir - it shares it,
for their heav'n, proph - ets, psalm-ists, seers, and sag - es,
fir - ma - ment, know with you, O God im - mor - tal,

know - ing ev - er - last - ing peace.
Christ has passed th' e - ter - nal gates.
all a - wait the glo - ry giv'n.
Je - sus Christ whom you have sent!

93 Alleluia! Give the glory

ALLELUIA! GIVE THE GLORY Irregular with refrain

Refrain

Al - le - lu - ia!_____ Al - le -
lu - ia!_____ Al - le - lu - - -
ia!_____ Give the glo-ry_____ and the
hon - or_____ to the Lord!_____

1 Where two or three are gathered in my name,
  there I am in the midst of them;
  there I'll be.

2 I am the vine and you are the branches.
  Abide in me and bear much fruit.

94 Sithi bonga (We sing praise)

SITHI BONGA Irregular

Zulu: Bo - nga
English: Praise God!

Zulu: Si - thi bo - nga bo - nga bo-nga bo - nga si - thi
English: We sing praise, O God, we sing your prais - es, we sing

bo - nga bo - nga bo - nga.
Praise God! Praise God! Praise God!

bo - nga si-thi bo - nga, si-thi bo - nga bo - nga bo-nga
prais - es, we sing prais - es. We sing praise, O God, we sing your

Njen-gen-yo - ni en - hle hla - be - le -
Like the birds of heav - en we____ sing

bo - nga; en - hle hla - be - le ... Si - thi
prais - es; heav - en, we sing praise. We sing

Text: George A. Mxadana; English paraphrase by S. T. Kimbrough, Jr.
Music: George A. Mxadana; arranged by Patrick Matsikenyiri

95 Jesus has done so much for me

I CANNOT TELL IT ALL* Irregular with refrain

*Original title

Text: traditional African-American spiritual
Music: traditional African-American spiritual; arranged by Tom Booth and Joyce Bailey
Copyright © 1997 Tom Booth. Published by OCP.

can - not   tell   it   all!

Verses

Solo

1 He brought me out   from   dark-ness in - to light!

Solo

2 He done so much for me   when he died   on Cal - va-ry!

All

I   can-not tell   it all!   I   can-not tell   it all!

Solo

1 He brought me out   from   dark-ness in-to light!

Solo

2 He done   so much for me when he died   on Cal-va-ry!

All   D.C.

I   can - not   tell   it   all!

96 Had God brought us out

DAYEINU 888. 3 with refrain

1 Had God brought us out of E-gypt and not fed us in the des-ert,
2 Had God fed us all with man-na and had not or-dained the Sab-bath,
3 Had God then or-dained the Sab-bath and not brought us to Mount Si-nai,
4 Had God brought us to Mount Si-nai and not giv-en us the To-rah,
5 Had God giv-en us the To-rah and not led us in - to Is-rael,

then it would have sat - is - fied us. Da - yei - nu.*

Refrain

Da - da - yei - nu, da - da - yei - nu,

da - da - yei-nu, da - yei-nu, da - yei-nu, da - yei-nu.

Da - da - yei - nu, da - da - yei - nu,

da - da - yei - nu, da - yei - nu, da - yei - nu!

*Pronunciation: Dah-yay-noo (a Hebrew word meaning "enough")

Text: from the traditional Passover text
Music: Israeli traditional; arranged by Marilyn Houser Hamm and James E. Clemens, 2006
Arrangement copyright © 2006 Marilyn Houser Hamm and James E. Clemens

Silence my soul

SILENCE MY SOUL 88. 44. 55. 4 with ostinato

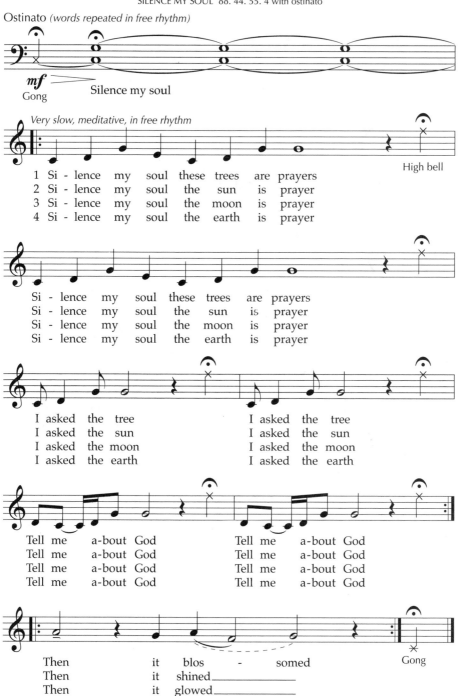

Ostinato *(words repeated in free rhythm)*

mf

Gong Silence my soul

Very slow, meditative, in free rhythm

High bell

1 Si - lence my soul these trees are prayers
2 Si - lence my soul the sun is prayer
3 Si - lence my soul the moon is prayer
4 Si - lence my soul the earth is prayer

Si - lence my soul these trees are prayers
Si - lence my soul the sun is prayer
Si - lence my soul the moon is prayer
Si - lence my soul the earth is prayer

I asked the tree   I asked the tree
I asked the sun   I asked the sun
I asked the moon   I asked the moon
I asked the earth   I asked the earth

Tell me a-bout God   Tell me a-bout God
Tell me a-bout God   Tell me a-bout God
Tell me a-bout God   Tell me a-bout God
Tell me a-bout God   Tell me a-bout God

Then   it blos - somed   Gong
Then   it shined_____
Then   it glowed_____
Then   it gave   life

Text: Rabindranath Tagore (verse 1); Seong-Won Park (verses 2–4)
Music: Francisco F. Feliciano

98 On the journey to Emmaus

COLUMCILLE Irregular

1 On the jour - ney to Em - ma - us with our
2 And our hearts burned with - in us as we
3 And that eve - ning at the ta - ble as he
4 On our jour - ney to Em - ma - us, in our

hearts cold as stone— the One who would
talked on the way, how all that was
blessed and broke bread, we saw it was
sto - ries and feast, with Je - sus we

save us had left us a - lone. Then a
prom - ised was ours on that day. So we
Je - sus a - ris'n from the dead; though he
claim that the great - est is least: and his

Text: Marty Haugen, based on Luke 24:13–35
Music: Irish traditional; arranged by Marty Haugen
Text and Arrangement copyright © 1995 GIA Publications, Inc.

stran - ger walks   with us and,   to our sur - prise,   he
begged him, "Stay   with us and   grant us your   word."   We
van - ished be - fore us we   knew he was   near—   the
words burn with - in us— let   none be ig - nored—   who

o - pens our   sto - ries and he   o - pens our   eyes.
wel - comed the   stran - ger and we   wel - comed the   Lord.
life in our   dy - ing and the   hope in our   fear.
wel - comes the   stran - ger shall___   wel - come the   Lord.

99 The Lord's my Shepherd

BROTHER JAMES'S AIR CM extended

1 The Lord's my Shep - herd, I'll not want. He
2 My soul he doth re - store a - gain; and
3 Yea, though I walk in death's dark vale, yet
4 My ta - ble thou has fur - nish - ed in
5 Good - ness and mer - cy all my life shall

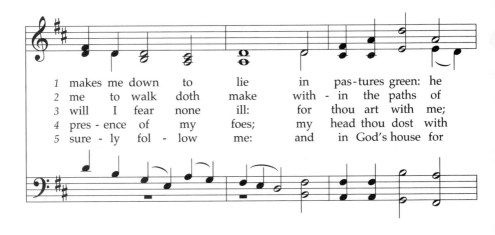

1 makes me down to lie in pas - tures green: he
2 me to walk doth make with - in the paths of
3 will I fear none ill: for thou art with me;
4 pres - ence of my foes; my head thou dost with
5 sure - ly fol - low me: and in God's house for

1 lead - eth me the qui - et wa - ters by; in
2 righ - teous - ness, ev'n for his own name's sake; with -
3 and thy rod and staff me com - fort still; for
4 oil a - noint, and my cup o - ver - flows; my
5 ev - er - more my dwell - ing - place shall be; and

Text: Psalm 23, *The Scottish Psalter*, 1929
Music: James Leith Macbeth Bain; harmonized by John L. Bell
Harmonization Copyright © 1998 WGRG The Iona Community (Scotland).
Used by permission of GIA Publications, Inc., exclusive agent.

1 pas - tures green: he lead - eth me the
2 in the paths of righ - teous - ness, ev'n
3 thou art with me; and thy rod and
4 head thou dost with oil a - noint, and
5 in God's house for ev - er - more my

1 qui - et wa - ters by.
2 for his own name's sake.
3 staff me com - fort still.
4 my cup o - ver - flows.
5 dwell - ing - place shall be.

100 O blessed spring

O WALY WALY LM

Dsus D G C G Dsus D7

1 O bless-ed spring, where word and sign em-brace us
2 Through sum-mer heat of youth-ful years, un-cer-tain
3 When au-tumn cools and youth is cold, when limbs their
4 As win-ter comes, as win-ters must, we breathe our
5 Christ, ho-ly Vine, Christ, liv-ing Tree, be praised for

Em Am Dsus D G/B D7/A G/B G

1 in- to Christ the Vine: here Christ en-joins each one to
2 faith, re-bel-lious tears, sus-tained by Christ's in-fus-ing
3 heav- y har-vest hold, then through us, warm, the Christ will
4 last, re-turn to dust; still held in Christ, our souls take
5 this blest mys-ter - y: that word and wa-ter thus re-

Em Bm Am/C G

1 be a branch of this life giv-ing Tree.
2 rain, the boughs will shout for joy a - gain.
3 move with gifts of beau - ty, wis-dom, love.
4 wing and trust the prom - ise of the spring.
5 vive and join us to your Tree of life.

Text: Susan Palo Cherwien
Copyright © 1993 Susan Palo Cherwien; admin. Augsburg Fortress
Music: English traditional; harmonized by James E. Clemens, 2004
Harmonization copyright © 2004 James E. Clemens

The risen Christ

BIRMINGHAM (CUNNINGHAM) 10 10. 10 10

1 The ris - en Christ, who walks on wound-ed feet from
2 The ris - en Christ, who stands with wound-ed side, breathes
3 The ris - en Christ, who breaks with wound-ed hand the
4 May we, Christ's bod - y, walk and serve and stand with

gar - den tomb through dark - ened cit - y street,
out his Spir - it on them to a - bide
bread for those who fail to un - der - stand,
the op - pressed in this and ev - ery land,

un - locks the door of grief, de - spair, and fear, and
whose faith still wa - vers, who dare not be - lieve, new
re - veals him - self, de - spite their lin-g'ring tears, en -
till all are blessed and can a bless - ing be, re -

speaks a word of peace to all who hear.
grace, new strength, new pur - pose they re - ceive.
flames their hearts, then quick - ly dis - ap - pears.
stored in Christ to true hu - man - i - ty.

Text: Nigel Weaver, 1993
Copyright © 1993 Nigel Weaver
Music: Joseph Funk, *Genuine Church Music*, 1st ed., 1832

102 Well met, dear friends

FRIENDLY MEETING CM extended

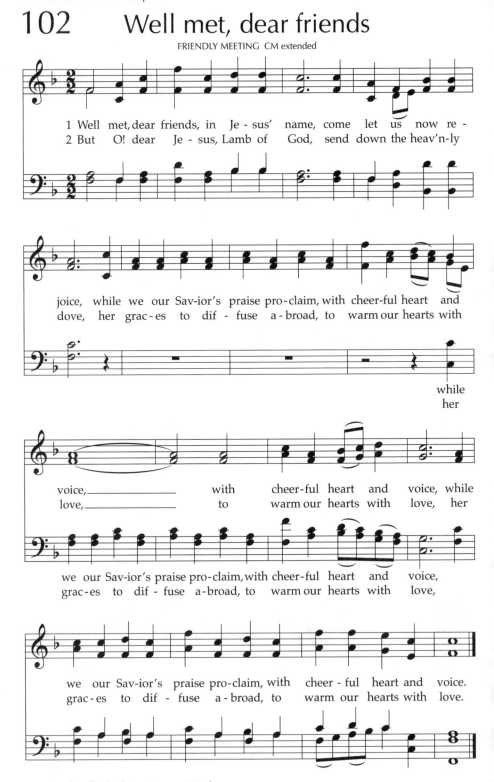

1 Well met, dear friends, in Je - sus' name, come let us now re -
joice, while we our Sav-ior's praise pro-claim, with cheer-ful heart and
voice, _____ with cheer-ful heart and voice, while
we our Sav-ior's praise pro-claim, with cheer-ful heart and voice,
we our Sav-ior's praise pro-claim, with cheer - ful heart and voice.

2 But O! dear Je - sus, Lamb of God, send down the heav'n-ly
dove, her grac - es to dif - fuse a - broad, to warm our hearts with
while
her
love, _____ to warm our hearts with love, her
grac - es to dif - fuse a - broad, to warm our hearts with love,
grac - es to dif - fuse a - broad, to warm our hearts with love.

Text: Jeremiah Ingalls, *The Christian Harmony*, 1805, alt.
Music: Jeremiah Ingalls, *The Christian Harmony*, 1805, alt.

Fire of God, undying flame 103

ABERYSTWYTH 77. 77D

1 Fire of God, un-dy-ing flame, Spir-it who in splen-dor came,
2 Strength of God, your might with-in con-quers sor-row, pain, and sin.

let your heat my soul re-fine till it glows with love di-vine.
For-ti-fy from e-vil's art all the gate-ways of my heart.

Breath of God, that swept in pow'r in the pen-te-cos-tal hour,
Love of God, your grace pro-found knows not ei-ther age or bound.

ho-ly breath, be now in me source of vi-tal en-er-gy.
Come, my heart's own guest to be; dwell for-ev-er-more in me.

Text: Albert F. Bayly
Music: Joseph Parry, *Ail Llyfr Tonau ac Emynau*, 1879

104 Come, O Spirit, come

Irregular

Ostinato

Db   Absus Ab7   Bbm   Ebm   Ebm/Db   Ab/C Eb7/Bb Ab

English: Come, O Spir - it, come.   Come, O Spir - it come.
Latin: Ve - ni, Spi - ri - tus.   Ve - ni, Spi - ri - tus.
Spanish: Ven, Es - pí - ri - tu.   Ven, Es - pí - ri - tu.

Db   Bbm7   Ebm   Ab7   Db   Ebm/Db   Db

Come, Spir - it, Come, Spir - it.   Come, Spir - it. Come.
Ve - ni, Spi - ri - tus. Ve - ni, Spi - ri - tus.
Ven, Es - pí - ri - tu. Ven, Es - pí - ri - tu.

Verses (sung over the ostinato)

1 Gift of God, be with__ us; build in us fire__ a - new.____
2 Gift of flame, come, burn in us; kin - dle fire__ with - in____ us.

3 Gift of wis - dom, come;____ give__ us eyes__ of liv - ing faith.
4 Gift of com - fort, come;____ fill us with peace and grace.____
5 Gift of heal - ing, come;____ strength-en us for__ your work.____

6 Gift of wind, blow through us, fill-ing us with__ your breath of life.
7 Gift of God, now come____ with__ the Fa-ther and Son;____

1 Gift of God,____ live with - in us. Gift of God, now come.
2 Gift of flame,____ live with - in us. Gift of flame, now come.

3 Gift of wis - dom, give us sight.____ Gift of wis - dom, come.
4 Gift of com - fort, dwell with - in us. Gift of com - fort, come.
5 Gift of heal - ing, strength-en us.____ Gift of heal - ing, come.

6 Gift of wind,____ fill us gent - ly. Gift of wind, now come.
7 Gift of God,____ Three yet One.____ Gift of God, now come.

Text: Paul F. Page
Music: Paul F. Page

Holy Spirit, truth divine

105

BUCKLAND 77. 77

1 Ho-ly Spir-it, truth di-vine, dawn up - on this soul of mine.
2 Ho-ly Spir-it, love di-vine, glow with - in this heart of mine.
3 Ho-ly Spir-it, power di-vine, fill and nerve this will of mine.

4 Ho-ly Spir-it, law di-vine, reign with - in this soul of mine.
5 Ho-ly Spir-it, peace di-vine, still this rest - less heart of mine.
6 Ho ly Spir-it, joy di-vine, glad-den now this heart of mine.

1 Voice of God and in-ward light, wake my spir - it, clear my sight.
2 Kin - dle ev - ery high de - sire, pu - ri - fy me with your fire.
3 Bold - ly may I al - ways live, brave-ly serve, and glad - ly give.

4 Be my law, and I shall be firm - ly bound, for - ev - er free.
5 Speak to calm this toss - ing sea, grant me your tran-quil - li - ty.
6 In the des - ert ways I sing; spring, O liv - ing wa - ter, spring!

Text: Samuel Longfellow, 1864
Music: Leighton George Hayne, 1863

106 Comme un souffle fragile
(Like a tender breath, stirring)

76. 76 with refrain

French: Comme un souf-fle fra-gi-le ta pa-ro-le se don-ne
English: Like a ten-der breath, stir-ring, your word breath-ing in us;

comme un va-se d'ar-gi-le ton a-mour nous fa-çon-ne.
like a pot-ter's clay ves-sel, your love mak-ing and shap-ing.

Interlude (instruments)

Text: P. Jacob; tr. Kenneth Nafziger and Randall Spaulding, 2006
Music: G. de Courréges
Text and Music copyright © 1988, 1994 Réveil Publications, Arc-en-ciel, Lyon, France
Translation copyright © 2006 Kenneth Nafziger and Randall Spaulding

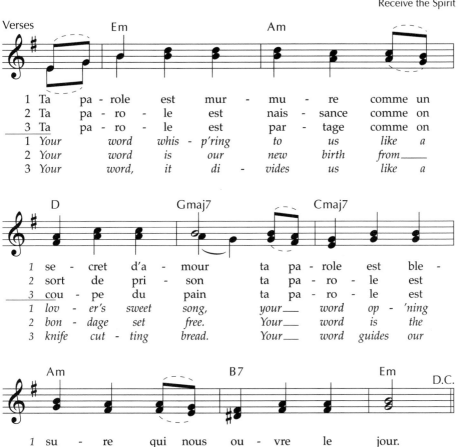

Verses

Em   **Am**

1 Ta   pa - role   est   mur - mu - re   comme un
2 Ta   pa - ro - le   est   nais - sance   comme on
3 Ta   pa - ro - le   est   par - tage   comme on
1 *Your*   *word*   *whis - p'ring*   *to*   *us*   *like*   *a*
2 *Your*   *word*   *is*   *our*   *new*   *birth*   *from____*
3 *Your*   *word,*   *it*   *di - vides*   *us*   *like*   *a*

D   **Gmaj7**   **Cmaj7**

1 se - cret   d'a - mour   ta pa - role   est   ble -
2 sort   de   pri - son   ta pa - ro - le   est
3 cou - pe   du   pain   ta pa - ro - le   est
1 *lov - er's*   *sweet*   *song,*   *your____*   *word*   *op - 'ning*
2 *bon - dage*   *set*   *free.*   *Your____*   *word*   *is*   *the*
3 *knife*   *cut - ting*   *bread.*   *Your____*   *word*   *guides*   *our*

Am   **B7**   **Em**   D.C.

1 su - re   qui nous   ou - vre   le   jour.
2 se - mence   qui pro - met   la   mois - son.
3 pas - sage   qui nous   dit   un   che - min.
1 *to*   *us*   *like*   *the*   *break - ing*   *of*   *day.*
2 *good*   *seed*   *and*   *the*   *har - vest*   *it*   *brings.*
3 *jour - ney,*   *re -*   *veal - ing*   *a*   *way.*

107 Fill now our life, O Lord

BILLING CM

1 Fill now our life, O Lord our God, in
2 Not for the lip of praise a - lone, nor
3 Praise in the com - mon things of life, its
4 So, gra - cious Lord, you shall re - ceive from

ev - ery part with praise, that
ev'n the prais - ing heart we
go - ings out and in; praise
us the glo - ry due; and

our whole be - ing may pro - claim your
ask, but for a life made up of
in each du - ty and each deed, though
so we shall be - gin on earth the

be - ing and your ways.
praise in ev - ery part.
hum - ble and un - seen.
song for ev - er new.

Text: Horatius N. Bonar
Music: Richard Runciman Terry; adapted by Compilers of *More Hymns for Today*, 1980
Copyright © Continuum International Publishing Group Ltd, The Tower Building, 11 York Road, London, England SE1 7NX.
Used by permission.

View the present

108

FRANKLIN PARK 85. 85. 88. 85

1 View the pres-ent through the prom-ise, Christ will come a-gain.
2 Probe the pres-ent with the prom-ise, Christ will come a-gain.
3 Match the pres-ent to the prom-ise, Christ will come a-gain.

Trust de-spite the deep-ening dark-ness, Christ will come a-gain.
Let your dai-ly ac-tions wit-ness, Christ will come a-gain.
Make this hope your guid-ing prem-ise, Christ will come a-gain.

Lift the world a-bove its griev-ing through your watch-ing and be-liev-ing
Let your lov-ing and your giv-ing and your jus-tice and for-giv-ing
Pat-tern all your cal-cu-lat-ing and the world you are cre-a-ting

in the hope past hope's con-ceiv-ing: Christ will come a-gain.
be a sign to all the liv-ing: Christ will come a-gain.
to the ad-vent you are wait-ing: Christ will come a-gain.

Text: Thomas H. Troeger
Music: Roy Hopp

109 Blessing and honor

ANCIENT OF DAYS Irregular with refrain

Text: Garry Sadler and Jamie Harvill
Music: Garry Sadler and Jamie Harvill

C   Csus   C (Fine)   Csus

2 Your

C

king - dom   shall   reign   o - ver   all   the   earth:

Bb/C   F/C   Gm/C   Bb/C   C no 3rd

sing   un - to   the   An - cient   of   Days.   For

C

none   shall   com - pare   to   your   match-less worth:

Bb/C   F/C   Gm/C   Bb/C   C no 3rd   C/E
D.S. al Fine

sing   un - to   the   An - cient   of   Days.

110 Alleluia! Gracious Jesus!

HYFRYDOL 87. 87D

1 Al - le - lu - ia! Gra - cious Je - sus! Yours the
2 Al - le - lu - ia! Not as or - phans are we
3 Al - le - lu - ia! Bread of an - gels, you on
4 Al - le - lu - ia! Christ e - ter - nal, noth - ing

scep - ter, yours the throne! Al - le - lu - ia! Yours the
left in sor - row now. Al - le - lu - ia! You are
earth our food, our stay. Al - le - lu - ia! Here the
can dis - rupt your reign. Al - le - lu - ia! Born of

tri - umph, yours the vic - to - ry a - lone!
near us; faith be - lieves, not ques - tions how.
sin - ful flee to you from day to day.
Ma - ry, heav'n and earth are your do - main.

Text: William C. Dix, 1867, alt.
Music: Rowland H. Pritchard, ca. 1830, *Cyfaill y Cantorion*, 1844; arranged by Ralph Vaughan Williams (*English Hymnal*, 1906),
        adapted 1951, *BBC Hymn Book*
        Arrangement copyright © Oxford University Press, London. Used by permission. All rights reserved.

Hark! the songs of peace - ful Zi - on thun - der
Though the cloud from sight re - ceived you when the
In - ter - ces - sor, friend of sin - ners, earth's Re -
Hu - man life you ful - ly en - tered, tend - ing

like a might - y flood; Je - sus, out of
for - ty days were o'er, shall our hearts for -
deem - er, plead for me, and the songs that
those we count the least, serv - ing both as

ev - ery na - tion you've re - deemed us as your own.
get your prom - ise, "I am with you ev - er - more."
sound in heav - en will re - peat your gra - cious plea.
Priest and Vic - tim in the eu - cha - ris - tic feast.

111　For me to live is Christ

ST MICHAEL (OLD 134TH) SM

1 For me to live is Christ: with
2 For me to live is Christ: from
3 For me to live is Christ: to
4 For me to live is Christ: for

him new life be - gins; his lov - ing touch re -
him true liv - ing springs; he comes, and with his
serve is now my aim; to help wher - ev - er
him my life I'll spend; my strength, my aim, my

news my mind and takes a - way my sins.
ra - diant love trans - forms all com - mon things.
there is need, and care in Je - sus' name.
hope, my Lord, from now till my life's end.

Text: Peter Henry Kelway Tongeman
Copyright © Peter Tongeman
Music: from melody for "Psalm 101" in *French-Genevan Psalter*, 1551; adapted by William Crotch;
arranged by Compilers of *Revised Church Hymnary*, 1927

My Lord, he is a-comin' soon 112

Text: Laura Winnen
Music: Jeff Cothran

113 I will stand in the congregation

STAND IN THE CONGREGATION 96. 96. 95 with refrain

1 I will stand in the con - gre-ga - tion and I will ex-
2 I will stand in the con - gre-ga - tion and I will__
3 We will join as a con - gre-ga - tion and we will ex-

alt__ you; I will stand in the con - gre-ga-
praise your name; I will stand in the con - gre-ga-
alt__ you; we will join as a con - gre-ga-

- tion and I will ex - alt__ you. Let the
- tion and I will__ praise your name. With your
- tion and we will ex - alt__ you. We will

chil-dren of your sal - va - tion lift their prais - es too!
peo-ple of ev - 'ry na - tion I will shout this praise!
sing__ as all cre - a - tion lifts the song a - new!

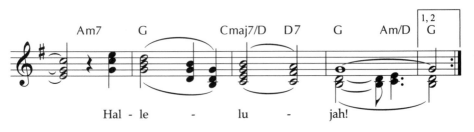

Hal - le - lu - jah!

Text: Bill Batstone
Music: Bill Batstone
Text and Music copyright © Maranatha Praise, Inc.; admin. Music Services.

114 God has chosen me

GOD HAS CHOSEN ME Irregular with refrain

1 God has cho - sen me, God has cho - sen me to
2 God has cho - sen me, God has cho - sen me to
3 God is call - ing me, God is call - ing me in

bring good news to the poor. God has cho - sen me,
set a - light a new fire. God has cho - sen me,
all whose cry is un - heard. God is call - ing me,

God has cho - sen me to bring___ new sight to those
God has cho - sen me to bring___ to birth a new
God is call - ing me to raise up the voice with no

search - ing for light: God has cho - sen me, cho - sen me:
king - dom on earth: God has cho - sen me, cho - sen me:
pow - er or choice: God is call - ing me, call - ing me:

Text: Bernadette Farrell
Music: Bernadette Farrell

115 Beauty for brokenness

GOD OF THE POOR Irregular

1 Beau-ty for bro-ken-ness, hope for de-
2 Shel-ter for frag-ile lives, cures for their
3 Ref-uge from cru-el wars, ha-vens from
4 Rest for the rav-aged earth, o-ceans and
5 Light-en our dark-ness, breathe on this

1 spair, Lord, in the suf-fer-ing____ this is our
2 ills, work for the crafts-men,____ trade for their
3 fear, cit-ies for sanc-tu-ar-y, free-doms to
4 streams, plun-dered and poi-soned, our fu-ture, our
5 flame, un-til your jus-tice burns____ bright-ly a-

1 prayer. Bread for the child-ren, jus-tice, joy,
2 skills. Land for the dis-pos-sessed, rights for the
3 share. Peace to the kill-ing fields, scorched earth to
4 dreams. Lord, end our mad-ness, care-less-ness,
5 gain; un-til the na-tions learn of your

1 peace, sun-rise to sun-set your king-dom in-
2 weak, voic-es to plead the cause of those who can't
3 green, Christ for the bit-ter-ness, his cross for the
4 greed; make us con-tent____ with the things that we
5 ways, seek your sal-va-tion and bring you their

1, 3

1 crease.
3 pain.

2, 4, 5

2 speak.
4 need.
5 praise.

Text: Graham Kendrick
Music: Graham Kendrick

Refrain

God of the poor, friend of the weak, give us com-pas - sion, we pray, melt our cold hearts, let tears fall like rain. Come, change our love from a spark to a flame.

4   D.S. | Final   Em D   G

116 I saw a tree by the riverside

TREE SONG* Irregular with refrain

1 I saw a tree by the
2 I saw a tree in the
3 I saw a tree in the

riv - er - side one day as I walked a - long,
win - ter - time when snow lay__ on the ground,
cit - y streets where build - ings__ blocked the sun;

straight as an ar - row and point-ing to the sky,
straight as an ar - row and point-ing to the sky; and
green and__ love - ly,__ I__ could__ see it gave

grow - ing tall and__ strong. "How do you grow so__
win - ter winds blew all a - round. "How do you stay so__
joy to ev - 'ry - one. "How do you grow in the

tall and strong?" I said to the riv - er - side
tall and strong?" I said to the win - ter - time
cit - y streets?" I said to the down - town

tree. This is the song that my tree friend sang to me:

*Original title

Text: Ken Medema
Music: Ken Medema

Refrain

I've got roots grow-ing down to the wa - ter, I've got leaves grow-ing up to the sun-shine, and the fruit that I bear is a sign of the life in me. I am shade from the hot sum-mer sun-down, I am nest for the birds of the heav-en. I'm be - com-ing what the Lord of trees has meant me to be— a strong young tree.

tree, a strong young tree,

a strong young tree.

117

How can I say

KOINONIA* Irregular

How can I say that I love the Lord whom I've
nev-er, ev - er seen be-fore; and for-get to say that I
love the one whom I walk be-side each and ev'-ry day? How
can I look up - on your face and ig - nore God's love? You I

*Original title

Text: V. Michael McKay
Music: V. Michael McKay

118 Keep your lamps trimmed

KEEP YOUR LAMPS Irregular with refrain

Text: African-American spiritual
Music: African-American spiritual; arranged by Andre Thomas
Arrangement copyright © 1982 Hinshaw Music, Inc.

-ver, the time is draw-ing nigh. Chris-tian

Keep your -ing, the

time is draw-ing nigh.

119 We believe, as one by one

74. 84

1 We be - lieve, as one by one and to - geth - er;
2 We be - lieve in Je - sus' name, Christ a - mong us,
3 We be - lieve that e - ven now God the Spir - it

Text: Joke Ribbers; English translation by Fred Kaan; French translation by Marc Chambron
Music: Bernard Smilde

the Lord is God, there is none else, a - men, a - men.
con-demned to death, but raised to life: Al - le - lu - ia!
will heal the world and heal us all: Peace be with us!

FRENCH

1 C'est la foi de tout chrétien,
c'est la nôtre:
Dieu tient le monde dans ses mains.
Amen, amen.

2 Nous croyons en Jésus-Christ,
mort sur la croix:
Pour toujours il a repris vie.
Alléluia!

3 Nous croyons en l'Esprit Saint,
qui, sans cesse,
vient pour guérir tous les humains,
et le monde.

Somebody prayed for me 120

SOMEBODY PRAYED FOR ME Irregular

1 Some-bod - y prayed for me, had me on their
2 My sis - ter prayed for me, had me on her
3 My broth-er prayed for me, had me on his

mind, took the time to pray for me.
mind, took the time to pray for me.
mind, took the time to pray for me.

I'm so glad they prayed, I'm so glad they prayed,
I'm so glad she prayed, I'm so glad she prayed,
I'm so glad he prayed, I'm so glad he prayed,

I'm so glad they prayed for me.
I'm so glad she prayed for me.
I'm so glad he prayed for me.

Additional verses:
My mother prayed ... My father prayed ... My Jesus prayed ...

Text: traditional African-American spiritual
Music: traditional African-American spiritual

121 Nothing is lost on the breath of God

GREEN LANE Irregular

1 Noth - ing is lost on the breath of God,
2 Noth - ing is lost to the eyes of God,
3 Noth - ing is lost to the heart of God,

noth - ing is lost for ev - er;
noth - ing is lost for ev - er.
noth - ing is lost for ev - er;

God's breath is love, and that love will re - main,
God sees with love, and that love will re - main,
God's heart is love, and that love will re - main,

hold - ing the world for ev - er. No
hold - ing the world for ev - er. No
hold - ing the world for ev - er. No

Text: Colin Gibson
Music: Colin Gibson

122 Let all creation dance

ST JOHN 66. 66. 88

1 Let all cre - a - tion dance in en - er - gies sub -
2 Our own a - maz - ing earth, with sun - light, cloud, and
3 Lift heart and soul and voice: in Christ all prais - es

lime, as or - der turns with chance, un -
storms, and life's a - bun - dant growth in
meet, and na - ture shall re - joice as

fold - ing space and time; for na - ture's art in
love - ly shapes and forms is made for praise, a
all is made com - plete. In hope be strong, all

glo - ry grows, and new - ly shows God's mind and heart.
fra - gile whole, and from its soul heaven's mu - sic plays.
life be - friend, and kind - ly tend cre - a - tion's song.

Text: Brian Wren
Music: *The Parish Choir Vol. 3*, 1851

Let us talents and tongues employ 123

LINSTEAD MARKET LM with refrain

1 Let us tal-ents and tongues em-ploy, reach-ing out with a
2 Christ is a-ble to make us one, at his ta-ble he
3 Je-sus calls us in, sends us out bear-ing fruit in a

shout of joy: bread is bro-ken, the wine is poured,
sets the tone, teach-ing peo-ple to live to bless,
world of doubt, gives us love to tell, bread to share:

Christ is spo-ken and seen and heard.
love in word and in deed ex-press.
God (Im-man-u-el) ev-'ry-where.

Refrain

Je-sus lives a-gain, earth can breathe a-gain,

pass the word a-round: loaves a-bound!

Text: Fred Kaan
Music: Jamaican folk tune; adapted by Doreen Potter

124 My soul cries out

STAR OF THE COUNTY DOWN 98. 10 8D with refrain

Em   C   D

1 My   soul cries out with a   joy - ful shout that the
2 Though   I am small, my God, my all, you
3 From the halls of power to the for - tress tower, not a
4 Though the na - tions rage from age to age, we re -

Em   C   D   Em

God of my heart is   great,   and my spir - it sings of the
work great things in me, and your mer - cy will last from the
stone will be left on stone. Let the king be - ware for your
mem - ber who holds us fast: God's mer - cy must de -

G   D   Em   C   Em

won - drous things that you bring to the ones who wait. You
depths of the past to the end of the age to be. Your
jus - tice tears ev - 'ry ty - rant from his throne. The
liv - er us from the con - quer-or's crush - ing grasp. This

G   D

fixed your sight on your ser - vant's plight, and my
ver - y name puts the proud to shame, and to
hun - gry poor shall weep no more, for the
sav - ing word that our fore - bears heard is the -

Em   C   D   Em

weak-ness you did not spurn, so from east to west shall my
those who would for you yearn, you will show your might, put the
food they can nev - er earn; there are ta - bles spread, ev - 'ry
prom - ise which holds us bound, 'til the spear and rod can be

Original title: "Canticle of the Turning"

Text: Rory Cooney, based on Luke 1:46-58
Music: Irish traditional; arranged by Rory Cooney
    Text and Music copyright © 1990 GIA Publications, Inc.

name   be   blest. Could the world   be   a - bout   to   turn?
strong   to   flight, for the   world   is   a - bout   to   turn.
mouth   be   fed,   for the   world   is   a - bout   to   turn.
crushed by   God,   who is   turn - ing the world   a - round.

Refrain

My   heart   shall   sing   of   the   day   you   bring.   Let the

My   heart   shall   sing   of   the   day   you   bring.   Let the

fires   of your jus - tice   burn.   Wipe a - way   all   tears, for the

fires   of   your jus - tice burn. Wipe a - way   all   tears, for the

dawn draws   near, and the   world is a - bout   to   turn!

dawn draws   near, and the   world   is   a - bout to turn!

WORSHIP RESOURCES

ADVENT: PREPARE THE WAY

125

God of Advent,
in the darkest days and nights of the year,
our hearts turn toward your promised light.

With the first faint glimmer of a single candle
dancing into the light of many bright flames,
our hope is ignited once more.

In these Advent days, lead us in your light
to a manger where the face of God
shines bright and clear. AMEN

126

Leader: God of faithfulness and truth,
you sent your servant John the Baptist
to preach in the desert
and summon the people to repentance.
ALL: *Make us and all things new,*
that in the wilderness of our hearts
we too may prepare a way
over which your Son may walk. AMEN

127

Leader: God of eternity,
when the voices of prophets are silent
and the faith of your people low;
when darkness has obscured light
and indifference has displaced zeal;
you see that the time is right,
and prepare to send your Son.
ALL: *Set us free from fear and faithlessness*
that we may be ready to welcome him
who comes as Savior and Lord. AMEN

128

Lord Jesus Christ,
Sun of righteousness,
shine on those who sit in darkness
and the shadow of death,
for you are the morning star of the universe,
the light and life of the world,
and we proclaim your glory,
now and for ever. AMEN

129

Leader: God of deep and dazzling darkness,
here on the edge of night
before we surrender our day
to silence and mystery,
we need to hear that you love us.

People: **We need to hear again your promise never to leave us;**
we need to hope in you.

Leader: Hear our prayer for all who weep tonight,
and those who wait beside the dying. *(pause…)*
Hear our prayer for frightened children,
for anxious parents and families in distress. *(pause…)*
Hear our prayer for nations at war,
for hungry refugees and those unjustly oppressed. *(pause…)*
Hear all our prayers.

All: *God of deep and dazzling darkness,*
our world is in your hands,
and so are we.
We rest in you.
In Jesus' name. AMEN

CHRISTMAS: CELEBRATE NEW BIRTH

130

Today, O God,
the soles of your feet
have touched the earth.
Today,
the back street, the forgotten place
have been lit up with significance.
Today,
the households of earth
welcome the King of heaven.
For you have come among us,
you are one of us.
So may our songs rise to surround your throne
as our knees bend to salute your cradle. AMEN

131

In the piercing cry of a baby
the blind, naked cry
of a human soul
entering the world
for the first time—
God comes to us
deliberately
vulnerable
and unclothed.

132

Leader: God and maker of all,
to redeem the world
you chose the most unsuspecting of women
to mother your Son
and by your choice gave new glory
to human flesh and earthly parenting.

ALL: *With the joy that was Mary's,*
may our souls magnify the Lord,
and our bodies be the means
through which you continue
the mighty work of salvation
for which Christ came. AMEN

133

To look on God's face
To dwell within the gaze
   of a destitute child
To see in his eyes flecks of light
   that will shatter darkness
To stand in the slight presence
   that will tear the world asunder
To bear witness to the ageless story of hope
   just now in infancy
To find footing along the path of salvation
   being unfurled, flung far and wide
To hear the mighty voice of God in whisper
and to know:
Now it begins.

134

Leader: God of Gabriel,
of birth and life,
hear our prayer:

Left: Like Mary,
make us bold
to question angels.

Right: Like Mary,
help us pray:
Your word be done.

Left: Like Mary,
stir our hearts
to ponder what you do.

Right: Like Mary,
prepare us for
the birth of Christ.

ALL: *God of Gabriel,*
of birth and life,
hear our prayer. AMEN

135

Leader: God of the dispossessed,
defender of the helpless,
you grieve with all the women who weep
because their children are no more.

ALL: *May we also refuse to be comforted*
until the violence of the strong
has been confounded,
and the broken victims have been set free
in the name of Jesus Christ. AMEN

136

Giver of life,
Bearer of pain,
Maker of love,
affirming in your incarnation
the goodness of the flesh,
may the yearnings of our bodies
be fulfilled in sacraments of love,
and our earthly embracings
be a foretaste of the pleasure
that shall be,
in the glory
of the resurrection body
of Jesus Christ. AMEN

137

Leader: Some want to keep a gospel so disembodied
that it doesn't get involved at all
in the world it must save.

People: **Christ is now in history.**
Christ is in the womb of the people.

ALL: *Christ is now bringing about*
the new heavens and the new earth!

EPIPHANY: WELCOME THE LIGHT

138

Almighty God,
clothe us in the mantle of praise
that we may always rejoice
in proclaiming your glory
and in receiving your blessings,
through Christ our Lord. AMEN

139

O God, the source of all insight,
whose coming was revealed to the nations
not among men of power
but on a woman's lap:
give us grace to seek you
where you may be found,
that the wisdom of this world may be humbled
and discover your unexpected joy,
through Jesus Christ. AMEN

140

Leader: Like the magi of old,
we bring our gifts to you, God-with-us.

People: **They are not gold, nor frankincense, nor myrrh,
but they declare our love and loyalty to you.**

ALL: *We pray that all we have and do
may be used for your service. AMEN*

MINISTRY OF JESUS: FOLLOW THE WAY

141

Leader: Gracious God,
we have come in search of Christ,
the Author of life.

ALL: *Open the Scriptures to us
that we might see Christ truly
and meet Christ face to face. AMEN*

142

Leader: From Bethlehem to Nazareth,
from Jordan to Jericho,
from Bethany to Jerusalem,
from then to now,

ALL: *Come, Lord Jesus.*

Leader: To heal the sick,
to mend the broken-hearted,
to comfort the disturbed,
to disturb the comfortable,
to cleanse the temple,
to liberate faith from convention,

ALL: *Come, Lord Jesus.*

Leader: To carry the cross,
to lead the way,
to shoulder the sin of the world
and take it away,

ALL *Come, Lord Jesus.*

Leader: Today,
to this place,
to us,

ALL: *Come, Lord Jesus. AMEN*

143

Holy One,
  untamed
  by the names
    I give you,
  in the silence
    name me,
  that I may know
    who I am,
  hear the truth
    you have put into me,
  trust the love
    you have for me,
      which you call me to live out
      with my sisters and brothers
      in your human family. AMEN

144

Leader:	The Spirit of God is upon us,
1:	to bring good news to the oppressed
2:	to heal the brokenhearted
3:	to announce freedom
	for prisoners and captives.
ALL:	*God has anointed us!*
Leader:	God has called us to comfort
	those who mourn,
1:	to give them flowers instead of ashes
2:	the oil of gladness instead of tears
3:	joyous praise instead of a faint spirit.
ALL:	*God has anointed us!*
Leader:	Those who were sad will be called
	Oaks of Justice, planted by God
1:	to honor God
2:	to rebuild what has been destroyed
3:	to rebuild what has been in ruins
	for many generations.
ALL:	*God has anointed us!*

145

Christ, whose insistent call
disturbs our settled lives:
give us discernment to hear your word,
grace to relinquish our tasks,
and courage to follow empty-handed
wherever you may lead;
that the voice of your gospel
may reach to the ends of the earth. AMEN

146

Leader: Christ our teacher,
you reach into our lives
not through instruction, but story.

ALL: *Open our hearts to be attentive:*
that seeing, we may perceive,
and hearing, we may understand,
and understanding, we may act upon your word,
in your name. AMEN

147

Leader: A blessing on you who are poor,
ALL: *yours is the kingdom of God.*
Leader: A blessing on you who mourn,
ALL: *you shall be comforted.*
Leader: A blessing on you who hunger for justice,
ALL: *you shall be satisfied.*
Leader: A blessing on you who make peace,
ALL: *you shall be called children of God.*
Leader: A blessing on you who are persecuted
for the cause of right,
ALL: *yours is the kingdom of heaven.*

148

Lord God, you ask us to love you
with all we possess.
Today we bring our minds to you,
just as they are:
open and closed; clear and confused;
pure and sullied; brilliant and slow.

We offer our minds
in all their complexity,
wonder, and power.
Rekindle them.
Remind us how to love you
with all of our being. AMEN

149

Leader: Eternal Spirit,
Life-Giver,
Pain-Bearer,
Love-Maker,
Source of all that is
and that shall be,
Father and Mother
of us all,
Loving God,
in whom is heaven:
ALL: *The hallowing of your name*
echo through the universe.

The way of your justice
be followed
by the peoples of the world.
Your heavenly will be done
by all created beings.
Your commonwealth
of peace and freedom
sustain our hope
and come on earth. AMEN

150

Leader: Jesus, you are the Great Questioner.
People: Keep our questions alive,
that we may always be seekers rather than settlers.
Leader: Guard us well from the sin of settling in
with our answers hugged to our breasts.
People: Make of us a wondering, far-sighted,
questioning, restless people.
ALL: Give us the feet of pilgrims
on this journey unfinished. AMEN

151

Leader: God, remind us to always look
for lonely coins, lost children,
people afraid they owe too much
to be loved again,
and those who are angry
because they've worked so long
in the vineyard.
People: Teach us to use our talents well,
hunt for the pearl of God's love,
and never ignore the treasure
buried in the fields
of our own church,
even if it feels like we need
to dig it up with a spoon!
ALL: AMEN

152

Leader: Loving Shepherd,
You gather the lambs in your arms
and call them each by name.
Move the hearts of your children
to know your love.
Light a spark in their hearts
that they may be like sunshine.
ALL: May they grow strong and gentle,
bold and wise.
And when they go wrong,
may they know your forgiveness.
This we ask for your love's sake. AMEN

153

1: The blessing of Martha's welcome,
2: the blessing of Mary's listening;
1: the blessing of action,
2: the blessing of reflection,
ALL: *the blessing of a God*
who is in each of these,
and in each one of us,
be with us all. AMEN.

154

God who will not be contained,
who breaks convention to surprise us with healing,
open our culture-bound eyes,
that we may move beyond our borders
to bring hope and healing to the world. AMEN

155

Leader: Jesus says: "I am the Bread of Life.
Whoever comes to me will never be hungry."
Teachers: We set the table for children, youth, and one another.
People: When we learn of Jesus, we're fed and nourished.
Teachers: Sweet rolls, tortillas, pascha, and pita —
Like bakers, we offer our imagination and experience.
People: We're hungry for good news, sweet wisdom, God's grace!
We accept this bread as a gift from God.
ALL: *Jesus is the Bread of Life. God is good!*
Come, eat, and be satisfied!

156

1: The face we have known now shines like the sun.
2: A voice says, "My Beloved; I am pleased with my own."
ALL: *With faces unveiled, we see God's glory shine.*
1: Jesus calls, "Get up and do not be afraid."
2: In the Spirit, we, too, are beloved, transformed.
ALL: *From glory to glory, we are beloved—we shine.*

157

Bless the work of our hands, O God.

Bless the hands that move earth, plant seeds and harvest,
hands with calluses and dirty fingernails, strong hands.

Bless the hands that drive cars and trucks and forklifts,
hands that spend time on computer keyboards, capable hands.

Bless the hands that manufacture and create,
working wood and metal and plastic, practical hands.

Bless the hands that wash, mop and scrub,
hands that know what to do with soap, determined hands.

Bless the hands that play instruments and hold paintbrushes,
hands that are creative tools, artistic hands.

Bless the hands that cook and feed, heal and nurture,
hands with a gentle touch, loving hands.

Bless the hands that give away money or food,
hands that are always trying to be empty, Christ-like hands.

Our hands do the work of your hands, O God our Creator. AMEN

158

May the seed of Christ's word,
   planted and watered by the Holy Spirit,
   find root and grow in your hearts.

159

May God write a message upon your heart,
   bless and direct you,
then send you out —
   living letters of the Word.

LENT: JOURNEY TO THE CROSS

160

God, who on foot
leads through unknown terrain,
teach us the trail head, the sharp turn,
   the thorn.
Teach us the fade of the path in
   the bramble;
make us to know your true face
   when we stumble.

Remember to find us.
Remember our name.
Remember your promise to walk with us home. AMEN

161

If you are delighted to be here,
   and if you are tired or troubled,
   you are welcome.
If your faith is strong,
   and if your faith is battered or frail,
   you are welcome.
If you are eager to praise God,
   and if you need to be quiet,
   you are welcome.
God welcomes us all to worship today
   and promises to meet us here.

162

Leader: God of all who thirst,
our hearts are parched from wandering in deserts
far from your life-giving springs.
Call us to your well.

ALL: *Fill our cups with your grace.*
Let your love overflow in our hearts,
and make us fully alive. AMEN

163

Lord, on the way to goodness,
when we stumble, hold us,
when we fall, lift us up,
when we are hard pressed by evil, deliver us,
when we turn from what is good, turn us back,
and bring us at last to your glory. AMEN

164

Leader: God who hears what is too deep for words,
beneath all our prayers for healing
you perceive the buried hope;
behind all our questions
you understand the hidden longing;
amidst all our singing
you hear the struggle to pray.

ALL: *God, who hears what is too deep for words, have mercy.*
Christ, have mercy. AMEN

165

Lord, teach us to forgive:
to look deep into the hearts
of those who wound us,
so that we may glimpse
in that dark, still water,
not just the reflection
of our own face
but yours as well. AMEN

166

You meet us in our hungering
with manna not of our making,
and in our thirsting
you surprise us
with unexpected wine.
You are the source
of our desiring
and the end
of all our longing.
O Giver of the feast
and ever-present Guest,
blessed be. AMEN

167

Go in the care of God,
who knows how we were made
and remembers that we are dust.
Go with the peace of God,
who forgives all our iniquity
and loves us with an everlasting love.

HOLY WEEK: BEHOLD THE LAMB

168

Leader: Lord Jesus Christ,
in this sacred and solemn week
when we see again the depth and mystery
of your redeeming love,

ALL: *help us to follow where you go,*
to stop where you stumble,
to listen when you cry,
to hurt as you suffer,
to bow our heads in sorrow when you die,
so that when you are raised to life again
we may share your endless joy. AMEN

169

God of judgment and mercy,
we draw near to you,
and pray that you will draw near to us.
Hear our confession.

Our hands need cleansing,
for they have participated in systems
of injustice and violence.
Our hearts need purifying,
for they have been wooed
by the power and hatred of the world.
God of mercy, hear our prayers
for healing and restoration.
(silent or spoken prayers)

As the cross looms before us,
may we walk in the pathway of Jesus,
who took on our brokenness,
yet pointed in hope toward your promise of new life.
In Jesus' name we pray. AMEN

170

Leader: Christ our Lord,
you refused the way of domination
and died the death of a slave.

ALL: *May we also refuse to lord it*
over those who are subject to us,
but share the weight of authority
so that all may be empowered
in your name. AMEN

171

Lord Jesus Christ,
Son of the Living God,
Washer of feet,
show us how to care for each other.
Teach us to love as you did.
Give us hands that are worthy
to serve in your name. AMEN

172

Before I take the body of the Lord,
before I share his life in bread and wine,
I recognize the sorry things within:
these I lay down.
(silent prayer)

The words of hope I often failed to give,
the prayers of kindness buried in my pride,
the signs of care I argued out of sight:
these I lay down.
(silent prayer)

The narrowness of vision and of mind,
the need for other folk to serve my will,
and every word and silence meant to hurt:
these I lay down.
(silent prayer)

Of those around in whom I meet my Lord,
I ask their pardon and I grant them mine,
that every contradiction to Christ's peace might be laid down.
(silent prayer)

Lord Jesus Christ, companion at this feast,
I empty now my heart and stretch my hands,
and ask to meet you here in bread and wine
which you lay down. AMEN

173

Here we are, God—a planet at prayer. Attune our spirits
that every heart might sing your hymn of peace.

Here we are, God—a militarized planet. Transform our fears
that we may convert our missiles into messengers of peace.

Here we are, God—a polluted planet. Purify our vision
that we may cleanse our lands, our waters and our life-giving air.

Here we are, God—an exploited planet. Heal our hearts
that we may provide for all an abundance of daily bread. AMEN

174

We pray, O Lord,
for all who must soon face death,
whether by illness, old age, or violence.
Strengthen them in their fear,
comfort them in their grief,
and give them some taste,
some inkling of the joy
you have prepared for them. AMEN

175

May the God of mercy,
who is well acquainted with grief,
bless us with gentle comfort
and healing for our sorrows.

176

Go into the world
with a daring and tender love.
The world is waiting.
Go in peace.
And all that you do,
do it for love.

EASTER: RISE TO NEW LIFE

177

Leader: I watch this morning
for the light that the darkness has not overcome.

People: **I watch for the fire that was in the beginning**
and that burns still in the brilliance of the rising sun.

Leader: I watch for the glow of life that gleams in the growing earth
and glistens in sea and sky.

People: **I watch for your light, O God,**
in the eyes of every living creature
and in the ever-living flame of my own soul.

Leader: If the grace of seeing were mine this day
I would glimpse you in all that lives.

ALL: *Grant me the grace of seeing this day.*
Grant me the grace of seeing. AMEN

178

Lord Jesus Christ,
we greet you.

The cross has not defeated you,
the grave has not kept you silent.
At the first dew of the morning,
you met our sister, Mary,
and called her by her name.

We are your family and friends,
and though numbed by your death
and aware of our complicity in it,
we come hesitantly but gladly,
to confirm the rumor
that you are alive.

Meet us as you met Mary,
with gentleness and resolution.
Speak our names quietly
in our hearts,
that we may proclaim your name boldly
on our lips. AMEN

179

Leader: O living God, who raised Jesus from the dead
we shout your great victory;
we sing hymns of praise!

People: **Even when our hearts are heavy**
and our eyes are dimmed by sorrow,
you are faithful.
You wipe away all tears
and bring joy in the morning.

Leader: Teach us, O God, to trust your gracious love,
to rest in your unfailing goodness,
to hope in your true promise,
that we may rejoice all our days
and share the good news:
death is defeated; all are made alive in you.

ALL: *Alleluia! Amen!*
Alleluia! Amen!

180

O God, the power of the powerless,
you have chosen as your witnesses
those whose voice is not heard.
Grant that, as women first announced
the resurrection
though they were not believed,
we too may have courage
to persist in proclaiming your word,
in the power of Jesus Christ. AMEN

181

We believe in a bright and amazing God
who has been to the depths of despair
on our behalf;
who has risen in splendor and majesty;
who decorates the universe
with sparkling water, clear white light,
twinkling stars and sharp colors,
over and over and over again.

We believe that Jesus is the light of the world;
that God believes in us, and trusts us,
even though we make the same mistakes
over and over and over again.

We commit ourselves
to Jesus,
to one another as brothers and sisters,
and to the Maker's business in the world.

182

Risen Christ,
when fear and doubt seem all that's left,
tell us again the stories of faith.
Touch us with your promised presence,
and set our minds at peace. AMEN.

183

Leader: Lord Jesus Christ,
you have ascended
beyond horizons which our eyes can see,
and further than the limits
which our minds can reach.
No longer restricted to one place,
you are seated on the throne of heaven,
and present in all places.

People: **We praise you,**
our glorious Lord and Savior,
and are forever glad
that now there is in heaven
One who understands and intercedes for us.

ALL: *Hallowed be your name!*
hallowed on earth as now in heaven. AMEN

184

Leader: The world is alive with your goodness, O God,
it grows green from the ground
and ripens into the roundness of fruit.
Its taste and its touch
enliven my body and stir my soul.
Generously given,
profusely displayed,
your graces of goodness
pour forth from the earth.

ALL: *As I have received*
so free me to give.
As I have been granted
so may I give. AMEN

185

To the Trinity be praise!
God is music, God is life
that nurtures every creature in its kind.
Our God is the song of the angel throng
and the splendor of secret ways
hid from all humankind,
but God our life is the life of all.

186

Lord, you are always doing miracles with common things.

You give us bread;
    we break it, butter it, taste it...know it is real.
But the mystery of seed, sprout, and leaven is hidden from us.

You give us bread;
    we break it, share its goodness, remember the miracle of Jesus' love.
But the mystery of how newness happens is hidden from us.

Lord of miracles in common things,
    as we eat, help us enter the mystery rejoicing. AMEN

187

Leader: O Holy Trinity,
    your dance of love invites us
    into the mysteries of death and life,
    pain and hope, despair and joy.
    When you offered yourself for us, O Christ,
    you gave life the victory over death,
    hope the victory over pain,
    joy the victory over despair.
    We thank you for creating the fruits of the earth, O God,
    and for feeding us these gifts of bread and wine
    that we might be satisfied by your unending love.
    Show yourself through our sharing of these gifts.

ALL: *Good Spirit,*
    come upon us now
    that we might take Christ's body and blood into our bodies.
    Dance in us, O Holy Trinity,
    as we eat this meal of grace,
    that our bodies may be joined in one Body,
    and that we might join our earthly dance with yours. AMEN

188

May the God who shakes heaven and earth,
whom death could not contain,
who lives to disturb and heal us,
bless you with power to go forth
and proclaim the gospel.

PENTECOST: RECEIVE THE SPIRIT

189

Leader: Come, Holy Spirit,
lamplighter, midwife of change,
comforter, disturber, inspirer, and advocate.

People: **Come, fill the church**
with the gifts earth
can neither produce nor afford.

Leader: Come, fill our lives
with that rich mixture of peace and restlessness,
calm and enthusiasm,
which are hallmarks of holiness.

ALL: *Come, promised Spirit of God,*
find your way and make your home among us. AMEN

190

Leader: People of God,
look about and see the faces
of those we know and love —

People: **neighbors and friends,**
sisters and brothers —
a community of kindred hearts.

Leader: People of God,
look about and see the faces
of those we hardly know —

People: **strangers, sojourners, forgotten friends,**
the ones who need an outstretched hand.

Leader: People of God,
look about you and see
all the images of God assembled here.

People: **In me, in you, in each of us,**
God's Spirit shines for all to see.

Leader: People of God, come.

ALL: *Let us worship together.*

191

O gracious God,
when you open your hand,
you satisfy the desires of every living thing.
Bless the land and waters;
give the world a plentiful harvest;
let your Spirit go forth
to renew the face of the earth. AMEN

192

Wind of God, blow far from us
all dark despair, all deep distress
all groundless fears, all sinful desires,
all false values, all selfish wishes.
(Silence)

Blow into us your holy presence,
your living love, your healing touch,
your splendid courage, your mighty strength,
your perfect peace, your boundless joy.
(Silence)

Wind of the God who loves and forgives us,
blow strong, blow fresh, blow now. AMEN

193

Christ the Word,
we long to speak effectively in your name,
but our words come out muddled and blunted.
Give us fresh, new-minted words,
that heart may speak to heart
and a new day begin. AMEN

194

Spirit of energy and change,
in whose power Jesus was anointed
to be the hope of the nations:
be poured out also upon us
without reserve or distinction,
that we may have confidence and strength
to plant your justice on the earth,
through Jesus Christ. AMEN

195

Leader: The blessing of God,
the shalom of God
the wildness
and the warmth of God,
be among us
and between us,
now and always.

People: **The divine Spirit**
dwells in us:

ALL: *Thanks be to God!*

196

Spirit of truth and judgment,
who alone can exorcize
the powers that grip our world:
at the point of crisis
give us your discernment,
that we may accurately name what is evil,
and know the way that leads to peace,
through Jesus Christ. AMEN

REIGN OF CHRIST: WATCH FOR GOD AMONG US

197

Sovereign Creator of earth and sky,
Savior always with us,
Spirit sweeping over the waters,
   renew our hearts today,
   surround us with grace,
   fill us with wonder and awe,
      so we may honor you
      with our gifts of love and praise
      and worship you with our whole life. AMEN

198

O Wonderful Weaver of the World,
help me to reach
from my separateness
to the unity of all creation.
I come as a single strand
and ask that you weave me
together with earth and sky,
eagle and tree,
water and fire,
red and black,
yellow and brown,
women and men,
young and old,
weak and strong
into your web of creation. AMEN

199

Leader: For all the saints who went before us
          who have spoken to our hearts and touched us with your fire,
ALL: *we praise you, O God.*
Leader: For all the saints who live beside us
          whose weaknesses and strengths are woven with our own,
ALL: *we praise you, O God.*
Leader: For all the saints who live beyond us
          who challenge us to change the world with them,
ALL: *we praise you, O God. AMEN*

200

In the face of all our realities:
we are the people who heal each other,
who grow strong together,
who name the truth,
who know what it means
to live in community,
moving towards a common dream
for a new heaven and a new earth
in the power of the love of God,

the company of Jesus Christ,
and the leading of the Holy Spirit.

201

Leader: All the broken hearts
shall rejoice;
all those who are heavy laden,
whose eyes are tired
and who do not see,
shall be lifted up
to meet with
the Motherly Healer.

People: **The battered souls and bodies**
shall be healed;
the hungry shall be fed;
the imprisoned shall be free.

ALL: *All earthly children shall regain joy*
in the reign
of the just and loving One
coming for you
coming for me
in this time
in this world.

202

Uniting God, we pray that the church may be one in Christ,
a true fellowship of the cloud of witnesses
who know their oneness in you
and speak the word of healing to this troubled world.
For the sake of Jesus Christ. AMEN

203

Thank you, God
that in every nation and every time
you accept all people who honor you.

Thank you for anointing Jesus of Nazareth
with the Holy Spirit and with power,
and for working through him to do good to all
and to heal those weighed down by evil.

Thank you for calling us to be your witnesses.
May we see and taste and know
Jesus' resurrection power,
his care for the world,
and his wisdom as Judge of the living and the dead.

Call us toward the great banquet of unity
you are preparing in the world
as all who have faith like Jesus
come into peace with one another
and peace with God. AMEN

204

ALL: *Giver of song,*
we give thanks for songs that surround us in the dark of night,
and for songs that waken us when morning breaks.

Leader: Give a song to all who need the comfort and reassurance of your presence:
those in trouble or in pain,
those overwhelmed by the demands of work,
those struggling with addictions,
and those whose past destroys their peace.

ALL: *Giver of song,*
sing through us
and bring your world to joy and rest. AMEN

Index of Copyright Holders for Hymns

44. Text and Music: © 1978 Stainer & Bell, Ltd. (admin. Hope Publishing Company, Carol Stream, IL 60188). All rights reserved. Used by permission.
45. Text: © SPCK, Holy Trinity Church, Marylebone Road, London NW14DU
Music: © 1998 Kevin Mayhew Ltd., admin. and sub-published in North America by GIA Publications, Inc., 7404 S. Mason Ave., Chicago, IL 60638. www.giamusic.com 800-442-1358 All rights reserved. Used by permission.
46. Trans and Arr: © Julia Smucker
47. Text and Music: © 1982, World Library Publications, 3708 River Road, Suite 400, Franklin Park, IL 60131-2158. All rights reserved. Used by permission.
48. Words and Music: © 1999 SongTalk Publishing Co. Used by permission.
49. Text and Music: © 1992 GIA Publications, Inc., 7404 S. Mason Ave., Chicago, IL 60638. www.giamusic.com 800-442-1358 All rights reserved. Used by permission.
51. Text and Music: © 1992 Jaime Cortez. Published by OCP Publications. All rights reserved.
52. Text and Music: © 1966, 1982 Willard F. Jabusch. Admin. OCP Publications. All rights reserved.
53. Text and Music: © 1991 Hope Publishing Company, Carol Stream, IL 60188. All rights reserved. Used by permission.
54. Text and Music: © 1986 by Desert Flower Music, P.O. Box 1476, Carmichael, CA 95609. Used by permission.
55. Text and Music: © 1996 Patricia J. Shelly
56. Text and Music: © 1993 GIA Publications, Inc., 7404 S. Mason Ave., Chicago, IL 60638. www.giamusic.com 800-442-1358 All rights reserved. Used by permission.
57. Text: © 2004 David Wright
Music: © 2004 James E. Clemens
58. Text: © 1981 International Committee on English in the Liturgy, Inc. All rights reserved.
59. Text: © 1994, World Library Publications, 3708 River Road, Suite 400, Franklin Park, IL 60131-2158. All rights reserved. Used by permission.
60. Text and Music: © 1986 North American Liturgy Resources. Published by OCP Publications. All rights reserved.
61. Text: Menno Simons
62. Text and Music: © 1994 Andrew Kreider
63. Text and Music: © Präsenz-Verlag Gnadenthal
64. Text and Music: © 1993 TEAM Publications. Published by OCP Publications. All rights reserved.
65. Text: © 1988, 1989, 2001 Jesse Manibusan and Rufino Zaragoza, OFM. Published by OCP Publications. All rights reserved.
Verse 4: © 1982 SOBICAIN
Music: © 1988, 1989, 1999 Jesse Manibusan. Published by OCP Publications. All rights reserved.
66. Text: 2005 David Wright
Music: 2005 James E. Clemens
68. Music: © 1987 Dinah Reindorf, admin. Augsburg Fortress.
69. Text and Music: © Oxford University Press. Used by permission. All rights reserved.
70. Text and Music: © 1988 Harold Flammer Music, a division of Shawnee Press, Inc. International Copyright secured. All rights reserved. Reprinted by permission.

71. Text and Music: © 1992 Hope Publishing Company, Carol Stream, IL 60188 All rights reserved. Used by permission.
73. Text and Music: © 1999, 2004 Augsburg Fortress. Used by permission.
74. Text and Music: © 1991 John C. Ylvisaker
Arr: © 2007 James E. Clemens
75. Text and Arr: © 2003 Augsburg Fortress. Used by permission.
76. Text: © 2000 GIA Publications, Inc., 7404 S. Mason Ave., Chicago, IL 60638. www.giamusic.com 800-442-1358 All rights reserved. Used by permission.
77. Text and Music: © 2002 Celah K. Pence
78. Text: © Leith Fisher
79. Music: © 1998 Atliers et Presses Taizé, Taizé Community, France. GIA Publications, Inc., exclusive North American agent, 7404 S. Mason Ave., Chicago, IL 60638. www.giamusic.com 800-442-1358 All rights reserved. Used by permission.
81. Text and Music: © 1969 Faith and Life Press
82. Text: © 1990 Barbara Woollett/Admin. Jubilate Hymns, Ltd./Hope Publishing Company, Carol Stream, IL 60188. All rights reserved. Used by permission.
83. Harm: © 1981 GIA Publications, Inc., 7404 S. Mason Ave., Chicago, IL 60638. www.giamusic.com 800-442-1358 All rights reserved. Used by permission.
84. Text: © 2004 Wild Goose Resource Group, Iona Community, Scotland. GIA Publications, Inc., exclusive North American agent, 7404 S. Mason Ave., Chicago, IL 60638. www.giamusic.com 800-442-1358 All rights reserved. Used by permission.
85. Text and Music: © 1996 Wild Goose Resource Group, Iona Community, Scotland. GIA Publications, Inc., exclusive North American agent, 7404 S. Mason Ave., Chicago, IL 60638. www.giamusic.com 800-442-1358 All rights reserved. Used by permission.
86. Text and Music: © 1996 Wild Goose Resource Group, Iona Community, Scotland. GIA Publications, Inc., exclusive North American agent, 7404 S. Mason Ave., Chicago, IL 60638. www.giamusic.com 800-442-1358 All rights reserved. Used by permission.
87. Arr: © 2005, World Library Publications, 3708 River Road, Suite 400, Franklin Park IL 60131-2158. www.wlpmusic.com All rights reserved. Used by permission.
88. Stanzas 2-4: © 1994, 2003 GIA Publications, Inc., 7404 S. Mason Ave., Chicago, IL 60638. www.giamusic.com 800-442-1358 All rights reserved. Used by permission.
Harm: © 2006 James E. Clemens
89. Text: © 1983 Hope Publishing Company, Carol Stream IL 60188. All rights reserved. Used by permission.
Music: © 2003 GIA Publications, Inc., 7404 S. Mason Ave., Chicago, IL 60638. www.giamusic.com 800-442-1358 All rights reserved. Used by permission.
90. Arr: © 2001 James E. Clemens
91. Text: © 2001, 2003 GIA Publications, Inc., 7404 S. Mason Ave., Chicago, IL 60638. www.giamusic.com 800-442-1358 All rights reserved. Used by permission.
93. Text and Music: © 1991 Ken Canedo and Bob Hurd. Published by OCP. All rights reserved.

Addresses of Copyright Holders for Hymns and Worship Resources

Mennonite Education Agency, 219 Brookwood Drive, Bluffton, OH 45817 866-866-2872 www.MennoniteEducation.org

Mennonite Publishing House, 616 Walnut Ave., Scottdale, PA 15683. 724-887-8500 www.mph.org

Music Services, Inc., 1526 Otter Creek Rd., Nashville, TN 37215 615-371-1320 www.musicservices.org

OCP, 5536 NE Hassalo, Portland, OR 97213 800-548-8749 www.ocp.org

Oxford University Press, 198 Madison Avenue, New York, NY 10016-4314 212-726-6000 www.oup.com/us

The Pilgrim Press, 700 Prospect Avenue, Cleveland, OH 44115 216-736-3764 www.thepilgrimpress.com

Howard S. Olson, 1925 Grand Cypress Lane, Sun City Center, FL 33573

Präsenz-Verlag, Gnadenthal, 65597Huenfelden, Germany, www.praesenz-verlag.de/en/

Schaff Music Publishing, 2919 Regency St., Houston, TX, 77045, (713) 728.1300

G. Schirmer, Inc. & Associated Music Publishers, Inc., 257 Park Avenue South, New York, NY 10010. 212-254-2100 www.schirmer.com

SECLI, Abbaye Sainte Scholastique, 81110 DOURGNE, France, secli@secli.cef.fr

Shawnee Press, Inc., c/o Music Sales Corporation, 257 Park Avenue South, New York, NY 10010. 212-254-2100 www.musicsales.com

Patricia J. Shelly, Bethel College, 300 East 27th Street, North Newton, KS 67117

Lois Siemens, Box 873, Kerrobet, SK S0L 1R0 Canada

Rebecca Slough, Associated Mennonite Biblical Seminary, 3003 Benham Avenue, Elkhart, IN 46517

Songtalk Publishing Co., c/o The Richmond Organization , 266 West 37th Street, 17th Floor, New York, NY 10018

Randall Spaulding, 3342 Glouster St., Sarasota, FL 34235. randy118@comcast.net

SPCK Publishing, 36 Causton Street, London SW1P 4ST, United Kingdom, +44 (0)20-7592-3900, www.spck.org.uk

Maren C. Tirabassi, 271 Lafayette Road, Portsmouth, NH 03801

The United Church Press, 700 Prospect Avenue, Cleveland, OH 44115 216-736-3764 www.united-churchpress.com

Wild Goose Publications, 4th Floor, Savoy House, 140 Sauchiehall Street, Glasgow G2 3DH, Scotland +44 (0)141-332-1090 www.ionabooks.com

Word Music Group, 20 Music Square East, Nashville, TN 37203 615-733-1880

World Library Publications, 3708 River Rd., Suite 400, Franklin Park, IL 60131, 800-621-5197 www.wlp-music.com

David Wright, 803 W. University Ave., Champaign, IL 61820 www.dwpoet.com

Index of Copyright Holders for Worship Resources

125. Copyright © Marlene Kropf

126. *Book of Common Order of the Church of Scotland*, copyright © 1994, Saint Andrew Press, Church of Scotland

127. *Book of Common Order of the Church of Scotland*, copyright © 1994, altered, Saint Andrew Press, Church of Scotland

128. Reprinted from *An Everyday Book of Hours* by William G. Storey © 2001 Archdiocese of Chicago: Liturgy Training Publications, 1800 N. Hermitage Avenue, Chicago, IL 60622. 1-800-933-1800. All rights reserved. Used with permission.

129. Copyright © Marlene Kropf

130. *Book of Common Order of the Church of Scotland*, copyright © 1994, Saint Andrew Press, Church of Scotland

131. Copyright © Kathy Keay

132. *Book of Common Order of the Church of Scotland*, copyright © 1994, Saint Andrew Press, Church of Scotland

133. Copyright © George Dupuy

134. From *Borrowed Light: Hymn Texts, Prayers and Poems* by Thomas H. Troeger (b. 1945). © 1994 Oxford University Press, Inc. Used by permission. All rights reserved.

135. Janet Morley, *All Desires Known: Third Edition*, copyright © 2006 Morehouse Publishing

136. Jim Cotter, *Prayers at Night's Approaching*, copyright © 1998 Morehouse Publishing

137. Oscar Romero, *Oscar Romero: Reflections on His Life and Writings* by Marie Dennis, Renny Golden, and Scott Wright. Copyright © 2000 Orbis Books

138. Reprinted from *An Everyday Book of Hours* by William G. Storey © 2001 Archdiocese of Chicago:

Liturgy Training Publications, 1800 N. Hermitage Avenue, Chicago, IL 60622. 1-800-933-1800. All rights reserved. Used with permission.

139. Janet Morley, *All Desires Known: Third Edition*, copyright © 2006 Morehouse Publishing

140. Copyright © Janeen Bertsche Johnson

141. John Rempel, from *Words for Worship* edited by Arlene M. Mark. Copyright © 1996 by Herald Press, Scottdale, PA 15683. Used by permission.

142. *Stages on the Way: Worship Resources and Readings for Lent, Holy Week and Easter*, © 2000, GIA Publications, Inc.

143. From *Guerillas of Grace* by Ted Loder copyright © 1984 Innisfree Press. All rights reserved. Reproduced by permission of Augsburg Fortress.

144. Copyright © Carmen Horst

145. Janet Morley, *All Desires Known: Third Edition*, copyright © 2006 Morehouse Publishing

146. Janet Morley, *All Desires Known: Third Edition*, copyright © 2006 Morehouse Publishing

147. 2001 © The Iona Community from *The Iona Abbey Worship Book*. www.ionabooks.com

148. Copyright © Gloria Y. Diener, ggdiener@ntelos.net, written for Mennonite Education Agency

149. Jim Cotter, *Prayers at Night's Approaching*, copyright © 1998 Morehouse Publishing

150. Copyright © Macrina Wiederkehr

151. Copyright © Maren C. Tirabassi

152. Copyright © Lois Kaufmann and Mary Lehman Yoder

153. 2001 © The Iona Community from *The Iona Abbey Worship Book*. http://www.ionabooks.com

154. Copyright © Lois Siemens

FIRST LINE INDEX OF HYMNS

- Regular-face type indicates the original language of a hymn
- Italic first lines are given for translations of hymns when the original language also appears
- Upper case is used for titles of hymns that differ from the first line (often a traditional title) and in cases where English words may be used with a musical setting in which a language other than English is given.
- Upper case in brackets indicates first lines of stanzas found in the accompaniment packet
- Songs with an asterisk (*) indicates an accompaniment that may be found in the Accompaniment Book.

A stable lamp is lighted* 25
Abres mis ojos* 65
ADVENT GATHERING SONG* 7
Alleluia (BYZANTINE) 87
Alleluia (DUNCAN) 17
Alleluia (JOYFUL)* 24
Alleluia (O FILII ET FILIAE) 88
Alleluia! Give the glory* 93
Alleluia! Gracious Jesus 110
ANCIENT OF DAYS* 109
Arise, your light is come! 30
As the pauper waits for plenty* 9
Auf Gott allein 70
Be joyful, oh heavens 18
BE THE CENTRE* 31
BEAUTIFUL STAR OF BETHLEHEM . . 32
Beauty for brokenness* 115
Blessed are they* 41
Blessed be the name* 75
Blessing and honor* 109
Brightest and best 29
C'est Dieu seul 70
C'est la foi de tout chrétien 119
Calm me, Lord* 45
CANTICLE OF THE TURNING* 124
CHILD OF THE POOR* 26
Christ is alive, and goes before us* 89
Come to me, come to us* 60
COME TO US* 60
Come unto me all ye that labor 48
Come! Walk in the light* 10
Come, bring your burdens to God 50
Come, come Emmanuel* 7
Come, Light of the world* 3
Come, O Spirit, come 104
Come, take and eat 46

Comme un souffle fragile 106
Create in me a clean heart* 62
DAYEINU* 96
Ears, eyes, hands, arms* 5
Eres santo, eres Dios* 34
Erfreue dich, Himmel 18
Fill now our life 107
Fire of God, undying flame 103
First born of Mary 37
For God alone my soul awaits 70
For me to live is Christ 111
From ashes to the living fount 59
Gentle God, when we are driven 71
GIFT OF GOD, BE WITH US 104
Gloria, Gloria, Gloria 23
Go, my friends, in grace 57
God has chosen me 114
GOD OF THE POOR* 115
God, fill me now 63
Hacia Belén se encaminan* 20
Had God brought us out of Egypt* . . . 96
Have mercy on us, Lord 67
[HE BROUGHT ME OUT FROM
DARKNESS]* 95
Helpless and hungry* 26
Here is the bread that is broken
for you* 77
Here to the house of God we come* . . . 53
Heri ni jina* 75
Herr, füll mich neu 63
Holy Child within the manger* 28
CAROL AT THE MANGER* 28
Holy Spirit, come to us* 79
Holy Spirit, truth divine 105
Hope is a candle* 15
Hosanna! Hosanna! 74

How can I say that I love the Lord* . . 117
How long, O Lord* 82
I CANNOT TELL IT ALL* 95
I saw a tree by the riverside* 116
I will come to you in the silence* 49
I will stand in the congregation* 113
[IN THE DAYS AHEAD, THE
    NATIONS WILL STREAM] * 10
Jesus has done so much for me* 95
Jesus is coming 73
Jesus walked this lonesome valley 80
Jesus, be the center* 31
Jesus, Jesus, oh, what a wonderful
    child* 19
[JESUS SAID, "I GIVE YOU"] * 79
Jesus, tempted in the desert 36
Keep your lamps trimmed and
    burning 118
Khudaya, rahem kar 67
KOINONIA* 117
Kyrie eleison* 68
Lay down your head, Lord Jesus
    Christ 85
Lè ou pote yon kado 43
Let all creation dance 122
Let justice roll like a river* 33
Let the children come to me* 47
Let us talents and tongues employ* . . 123
Like a tender breath, stirring 106
Lord Jesus, as the shadows long 78
Lord, have mercy* 68
Love the Lord your God* 55
Magnificat* 12
Maranatha, come* 2
Mi alma espera solo 70
My Lord, he is a-comin' soon* 112
My soul cries out* 124
No wind at the window* 11
Nothing is lost on the breath of God . . 121
O blessed spring where word and
    sign 100
O God, how we have wandered 58
O God, to whom then shall I turn? 61
O Lamb of God* 69
Oh, beautiful Star of Bethlehem 32
Oh, how good is Christ the Lord* 90

Oh, qué bueno es Jesús* 90
On the journey to Emmaus* 98
OPEN MY EARS, OPEN MY EYES* 5
Open my eyes, Lord* 65
Our Father, which art in heaven* 42
PAVE THE WAY WITH BRANCHES* . . 73
Peace before us* 16
Praise the one who breaks the
    darkness 1
Prepare a room for me 76
Prepare the way of the Lord* 14
Quièn dicen que soy yo* 51
Rejoice, rejoice the Savior comes 4
Remember me 83
Remember this when you bring a gift 43
Save us, O Lord* 6
Silence, my soul these trees 97
Sing a different song now* 27
Sing we a song of high revolt 13
Sing we the virgin Mary 21
Sing with all the saints in glory 92
Sithi bonga 94
So much wrong and so much
    injustice 84
Som'landela 40
Somebody prayed for me 120
STAND IN THE CONGREGATION* . . 113
Star of the morning 91
[TAKE FROM ME YOUR HOLY
    FEASTS] * 33
Thank you for the night 86
THAT EASTER MORN, AT BREAK
    OF DAY 88
The Lord's my Shepherd 99
THE LORD'S PRAYER* 42
The risen Christ, who walks 101
THE SUMMONS* 39
THE TREE SONG* 116
There is a well* 64
There were angels hov'ring 'round . . . 22
THIS IS A DAY OF NEW
    BEGINNINGS* 89
Thou, O Christ, my Lord and King . . . 35
Tu es saint et abundance* 34
Un pozo hay* 64
Unless a grain of wheat* 56

View the present through the
promise 108

Vin pran, vin pran 46

*Walking slowly unto Beth'lem** 20

We are often tossed and driv'n 72

WE ARE THE LIGHT OF THE
WORLD* 41

We believe, as one by one 119

We sing praise, O God 94

We will follow 40

WE'LL UNDERSTAND IT BETTER
BY AND BY 72

Well met, dear friends 102

What does the Lord require of you ... 54

Whatsoever you do 52

When Jesus worked here on earth 38

When Jesus the healer passed through
Galilee* 44

When we are tempted to deny your
son 81

[WHERE TWO OR THREE ARE
GATHERED] * 93

While I keep silence 66

*Who do you say that I am** 51

Will you come and follow me* 39

Wild and lone, the prophets voice* 8

Woza nomthwalo wakho 50

Ya hamalaLah* 69

You are holy, you are whole* 34

YOU ARE MINE* 49

ACTS OF WORSHIP INDEX FOR HYMNS

GATHERING

Alleluia! Give the glory 93
Come! Walk in the light 10
Come, bring your burdens to God 50
Come, O Spirit, come 104
For God alone my soul awaits
   in silence 70
Here to the house of God we come ... 53
Herr, füll mich neu 63
Holy Spirit, truth divine 105
Jesus, be the center 31
Open my ears, open my eyes 5
Prepare the way of the Lord 14
Silence, my soul these trees 97
Well met, dear friends 102

PRAISING

Alleluia! 17
Blessing and honor 109
You are holy 34
Erfreue dich 18
Fill now our life 107
I will stand in the congregation 113
Jesus has done so much for me 95
Jesus, Jesus, oh, what a wonderful
   Child 19
Magnificat 12
My soul cries out 124
Praise the one who breaks the
   darkness 1
Sing with all the saints in glory 92
Sithi Bonga 94
Star of the morning 91

CONFESSING

Create in me a clean heart 62
Fire of God, undying flamr 103
How long, O Lord 82
Khudaya, rahem kar 67
Kyrie Eleison 68
O God, how we have wandered 58
O God, to whom then shall I turn? 61
Abres Mis Ojos 65
Save us, O Lord 6
When we are tempted 81
While I keep silence 66
Ya hamalaLah 69

PROCLAIMING Creation

Let all creation dance 122
I saw a tree by the riverside 116
Silence, my soul these trees 97

PROCLAIMING God

Had God brought us out of Egypt 96
Nothing is lost on the breath of God .. 121
Our Father, who art in heaven 42

PROCLAIMING Jesus' Advent
(See ADVENT: 1-16)

Arise, your light is come! 30
Keep your lamps trimmed and
   burning 118
My soul cries out 124

PROCLAIMING Jesus' Birth
(See CHRISTMAS: 17-29)

Brightest and best 29
Magnificat 12
Oh, beautiful star of Bethlehem 32

PROCLAIMING Jesus' Epiphany
(See EPIPHANY: 30-35)

Come, Light of the World 3
Come! Walk in the light 10

PROCLAIMING Jesus' Life/Ministry
(See JESUS LIFE/MINISTRY: 36-58)

From ashes to the living fount 59
Prepare a room for me 76
Here is the bread 77

PROCLAIMING Jesus' Passion/Death
(See HOLY WEEK: 74-86)

Jesus has done so much for me 95
Ya hamalaLah 69

PROCLAIMING Jesus' Resurrection
(See EASTER: 87-102)

Alleluia! 17
Alleluia (JOYFUL) 24
Blessing and honor 109
I will stand in the congregation 113
Let us talents and tongues employ ... 123
Nothing is lost on the breath of God .. 121

PROCLAIMING Jesus' Ascension

Alleluia! Gracious Jesus! 110
Blessing and honor 109

PROCLAIMING Jesus' Presence in Spirit
(See PENTECOST: 103-108)

Jesus, be the center 31
Love the Lord your God 55

PROCLAIMING Christ's 2nd Coming
(See REIGN OF CHRIST: 109-125)

Rejoice, rejoice, the Savior comes 4
Open my ears, open my eyes 5

Maranatha, come 2
Come, Light of the world 3
Prepare the way of the Lord 14
Star of the morning 91

PROCLAIMING Trinity
Come, O Spirit, come 104
We believe, as one by one 119

PROCLAIMING Activity of Spirit
(See PENTECOST: 103-108)

PROCLAIMING Church
Blessed are they 41
The risen Christ, who walks 101
We believe, as one by one 119
Well met, dear friends 102

PROCLAIMING Word of God
Alleluia! 17
Alleluia (BYZANTINE) 87
Comme un souffle fragile 106
Firstborn of Mary 37
Holy Spirit, truth divine 105

PROCLAIMING Kingdom
(See REIGN OF Christ: 109-125)

AFFIRMING FAITH
For me to live is Christ 111
Quién dicen que soy yo? 51
We believe, as one by one 119

PRAYING
Beauty for brokenness 115
Come, Light of the world 3
Gentle God, when we are driven 71
Herr, full mich neu 63
Our Father, who art in heaven 42
Silence, my soul these trees 97
Somebody prayed for me 120
Thou, O Christ, my Lord and King . . . 35
When Jesus the healer 44

OFFERING
Le ou pote yon kado 43
Let us talents and tongues employ . . . 123

WITNESSING
Beauty for brokenness 115
Blessed are they 41
God has chosen me 114
How can I say that I love the Lord . . . 117
Jesus has done so much for me 95
Let justice roll like a river 33
So much wrong 84
Som'landela 40
The risen Christ, who walks 101

What does the Lord require of you . . . 54
Whatsoever you do 52

SENDING
Go, my friends, in grace 57
Let us talents and tongues employ . . . 123
Peace before us 16

BAPTISM
For me to live is Christ 111
O blessed spring 100
Star of the morning 91
There is a well 64
Unless a grain of wheat 56

FOOT WASHING
Holy Spirit, come to us 79
Lord Jesus, as the shadows long 78

COMMUNION
Come to me, come to us 60
Here is the bread 77
Let us talents and tongues employ . . . 123
Our Father, who art in heaven 42
Prepare a room for me 76
Vin pran 46
You are holy 34

FAITH JOURNEY
Christ is alive 89
Come unto me 48
Heri ni jina 75
How long, O Lord 82
I saw a tree by the riverside 116
I will come to you in the silence 49
Jesus walked this lonesome valley 80
Let the children come to me 47
Nothing is lost on the breath of God . . 121
O blessed spring 100
Remember me 83
Som'landela 40
The Lord's my shepherd 99
There are angels hov'ring 'round 22
We are often tossed and driv'n 72
When we are tempted 81
While I keep silence 66
Will you come and follow me 39
Woza nomthwalo wakho 50

MORNING/ EVENING
Go, my friends, in grace 57
Star of the morning 91
Thank you for the night 86

ACTS OF WORSHIP INDEX FOR WORSHIP RESOURCES

GATHERING

God of Advent 125
God of faithfulness and truth 126
God of eternity 127
Today, O God 130
To look on God's face 133
O God, the source of all insight 139
Gracious God, we have come 141
From Bethlehem to Nazareth 142
Christ our teacher 146
If you are delighted to be here 161
Lord Jesus Christ, in this sacred 168
I watch this morning 177
Lord Jesus Christ, we greet you 178
O living God, who raised Jesus 179
Come, Holy Spirit 189
People of God, look about 190
Sovereign Creator of earth and sky .. 197

PRAISING

Lord Jesus Christ, Sun of
    righteousness 128
Today, O God 130
God and maker of all 132
Almighty God, clothe us 138
You meet us in our hungering 166
O living God, who raised Jesus 179
Lord Jesus Christ, you have
    ascended 183
The world is alive with your
    goodness 184
To the Trinity be praise! 185
Sovereign Creator of earth and sky .. 197
For all the saints 199
Thank you, God 203

CONFESSING

God of faithfulness and truth 126
Lord God, you ask us to love you ... 148
Jesus, you are the Great Questioner .. 150
God, who on foot 160
God of all who thirst 162
Lord, on the way to goodness 163
God, who hears what is too deep 164
Lord, teach us to forgive 165
God of judgment and mercy 169
Before I take the body of the Lord ... 172
Wind of God, blow far from us 192

AFFIRMING FAITH

Lord Jesus Christ, Sun of
    righteousness 128

In the piercing cry of a baby 131
The Spirit of God is upon us 144
A blessing on you who are poor 147
The face we have known 156
You meet us in our hungering 166
We believe in a bright and amazing
    God 181
Lord Jesus Christ, you have
    ascended 183
To the Trinity be praise! 185
The blessing of God 195
In the face of all our realities 200
All the broken hearts shall rejoice 201

PRAYING

God of deep and dazzling darkness .. 129
God of Gabriel 134
God of the dispossessed 135
Giver of life 136
O God, the source of all insight 139
Gracious God, we have come 141
From Bethlehem to Nazareth 142
Holy One, untamed 143
Christ our teacher 146
Eternal Spirit, Life-Giver 149
God, remind us to always look 151
God, who on foot 160
Christ our Lord, you refused 170
Lord Jesus Christ, Son of 171
Here we are, God – a planet 173
We pray, O Lord 174
Risen Christ, when fear and doubt ... 182
Come, Holy Spirit 189
O gracious God 191
Spirit of truth and judgment 196
O Wonderful Weaver 198
Giver of song 204

OFFERING

Like the magi of old 140
The world is alive with your
    goodness 184
O gracious God 191

WITNESSING

God of the dispossessed 135
Some want to keep a gospel 137
Christ, whose insistent call 145
God who will not be contained 154
Bless the work of our hands 157
May God write a message 159
Lord Jesus Christ, we greet you 178

O God the power of the powerless . . . 180
May the God who shakes heaven
   and earth 188
Christ the Word, we long to speak . . . 193
Spirit of energy and change 194
Uniting God, we pray 202

SENDING
A blessing on you who are poor 147
The blessing of Martha's welcome . . . 153
May the seed of Christ's word 158
May God write a message 159
Go in the care of God 167
May the God of mercy 175
Go into the world 176
May the God who shakes heaven
   and earth 188
The blessing of God 195
Giver of song 204

BAPTISM
To look on God's face 133
Holy One, untamed 143
The Spirit of God is upon us 144

COMMUNION
You meet us in our hungering 166
Lord Jesus Christ, Son of 171
Before I take the body of the Lord . . . 172
Lord, you are always doing
   miracles 186
O Holy Trinity, your dance of love . . . 187

FAITH JOURNEY
Giver of life 136
Christ, whose insistent call 145
Jesus, you are the Great Questioner . . 150
Loving Shepherd 152
Jesus says, "I am the Bread of Life" . . 155
Bless the work of our hands 157
God, who on foot 160
We pray, O Lord 174

MORNING AND EVENING
Lord Jesus Christ, Sun of
   righteousness 128
God of deep and dazzling darkness . . 129
I watch this morning 177
Giver of song 204